The Black Wall
Paul Hardman
ISBN: 978-1-8382744-6-7

Published By: -

i2i

PUBLISHING

i2i Publishing. Manchester.
www. i2ipublishing. co. uk

The Black Wall

Foreword

Set in the early 80s, The Black Wall tells of the activities and behaviours of a group of boys on the streets of Salford. Their pastimes, often hilarious, but also tinged with sadness and peril on occasions, certainly brought a smile to my face and the odd tear to the eye whilst writing it. Hopefully you, the reader, will also enjoy the chapters as you turn the pages.
Thanks to the illustrator, Michael Laing and also to the setters, Mark and Danielle Harrison for their help in the production of the book.

Paul Hardman, B. A. Hons. August, 2020.

CHAPTER ONE

'Cromson Street'

Hello, my name is Tod. This is The Black Wall, and what a story it holds!

Within each brick of this end terrace there is an episode, and it will become apparent that life here during teenage years was, on the whole, a ball, albeit with darker moments at times. . .

There were seven of us, Smithy, Gazzer, Diesel, Murph, Larry, Chad, and myself. We were called the Crommy Boys, as the street where we hung out was called Crompson Street in Salford, near Manchester.

Smithy was the clever one in the gang. He wore jam jar glasses and when he spoke, saliva emerged from the side of his mouth and his uncut finger nails harboured a black substance resembling soil, which personally turned my stomach when he chewed them. It was the early 80s when we had our day at the Wall and computers were in vogue. Smithy, of course, had the best one in the group. He bored us at times, talking about programmes on his desk top. Diesel and Gazzer would often yawn openly during a lecture which was met by two fingers from him, amidst the roar of laughter! As we will see, he could at times suffer from delusions of grandeur.

Gazzer was always out and about on the Street. His main interest was the Royal Marines followed closely by girls, Diesel's motor bike and break dance. He would do 'boot runs' along the Liverpool Manchester road, in preparation for his life in the forces. Sometimes returning back to the Wall after his run, he would say that one day it would all be worth it. Stocky in build, with a shaved head and a determined look, we knew one day he would make it.

Diesel was a good mate of Gazzer's and wanted to be in the marines also. Having a shaved head and often seen flexing his muscles, he would talk of which places he would visit in the marines when he left school which he disliked. He had a crosser motor bike as previously mentioned and that, together with his dream of being a marine, his fishing, break dance and girls of course, were all he was concerned about. An interest in girls was a common denominator amongst the lads, not surprisingly, generally speaking it turned out. .

Murph was not the sharpest tool in the shed, you might say, but a laugh nevertheless. He had broken his arm in an episode with a rival gang, which, I'm sure we'll touch on during our time together, and blamed his subsequent U grades in his 1983 finals on the poorly attended time at school after this incident. To be truthful, his interests lay outside the class room and more in the undertakings of the Street and chatting up members of the opposite sex, which rarely achieved its aim, unfortunately for him.

Although dragged into our escapades, Larry was the sensible member of the team and adored his horse, Snow Flake. He would always be found at the farm on Clough Lane on a Saturday and Sunday, tending to the mare, making sure she was well turned out. He got stick from the lads, as you may imagine, and the mention of the glue factory, where Snow Flake would ultimately end her days, brought tears to our eyes and to his, for different reasons. Looking back it was a touch cruel, perhaps. . .

Chad was the cool dude in the group. Always sporting a Pringle or Slazenger jumper of fascinating colours and hand in hand with the best looking girl in the street, Suzy, he would laugh and joke at the Wall, talking about his experiences of the day with the others. Although he was no angel, it must be said, he avoided one or two of our more 'adventurous' activities which the years at the Black Wall bestowed upon us.

CHAPTER TWO

'The rubber brick'

We were all proud of our name, the Crommy Boys as we were of the Black Wall but so were the other gangs in the area such as the Woodland Crew, who met up at Wood Oak Fields over Clough Lane.

Being so territorial, as we were, friction between gangs ensued, leading to some interesting activity. One such outcome of this rivalry was the night of the rubber brick at the end of September 1982.

Woodland outnumbered us and had some nasty characters in their ranks. One of the crowd there, called Rammy, who was feared by all in his school, and even those in the Woodland gang itself, always saw the Black Wall as a threat and one night decided to do something about it, together with his crew.

Spending as little time on homework as possible, I and the others met at the Wall around seven o'clock that night. We were all there and Chad was telling us how he had bunked off maths that morning and met up with Suzy behind the news agent's near the school. Murph commented that he did not even know who his maths teacher was, which aroused much laughter.

Amidst the laughter, however, something was brewing on the horizon. Crossing Clough Lane and making their way to Cromson Street were about thirteen lads, headed by Rammy, holding a rubber brick, which are usually used in swimming pools when diving whilst wearing a pair of pyjamas! We had certainly never seen one in the street before! "Have you got your trainers on, Tod?" asked Gazzer, sounding a little serious, for once. Murph laughed, not fully understanding the situation, I felt, at the time, and Larry looked terrified. "OK, let's get on our way!" shouted Diesel. I looked at my Adidas Sambas and ran as fast as my feet could carry me. I could hear "Crommy Boys, you're going down!" and "Hope you like hospital food! "A little confused and afraid, I headed for the back entry or alley way, followed by Murph and Smithy.   Gazzer, Diesel and Larry sprinted in the opposite direction behind the old electric station. Chad just disappeared, as Chad usually did in these kinds of situations. I do not know where he got to.

What would Woodland do? Which direction would they go in? Would they split up? Who would get it and how bad would it be? A host of questions was going through my mind amidst the threatening cries and chaos.

"Not so funny after all eh, Tod?"shouted Murph as we fled down the cobbled entry.

"Why do you always question the obvious?" murmured Smithy, struggling for breath.

Personally, I had no time for conversations, especially as the whole lot of Woodland had decided to follow me, Murph and Smithy. I turned quickly around and could make out a bunch of silhouettes heading towards us and they were catching up because Smithy was not the fittest person in the world and I was slowing the pace, so he could keep up. Rammy's voice was very prominent. "You're going to get the brick; you're going to get the brick my friend!" he yelled. At this point things were not looking too good, it had to be said. I was being chased by a crowd of lunatics with a mate who did not really comprehend the severity of the situation and another who could not keep up. A plan was needed and needed quickly.

The poorly lit back entry afforded us a choice of back gardens, and seeing one with a rickety old gate, I grabbed the handle and fled down the garden path, around the house and into the front garden which, in turn, led to Cromson Street. All was going as well as it could, under the circumstances, when suddenly a huge problem faced us. A five-to-six-foot hedge row and a garden gate with a padlock on it! I had seen the garden a thousand times on the Street, but all looked so differently from a dimly lit back entry leading onto it, together with all the other problems involved. We obviously could not turn back, courtesy of Rammy and his band of merry men. "Give me a leg up, Murph, "I asked, which was duly given. I clambered over the hedge, beads of sweat dripping from my brow, followed by Smithy, gasping for air.

The pounding of feet on the back path was getting louder and the aggressive shouting noisier as Smithy and I grappled with Murph's arms to get him over the hedge row. "Just a bit more Murph!" I cried in desperation, when, suddenly, the rubber brick came flying into his head, causing him to fall back and twist his arm in the process.

"We've got his scalp lads!" Rammy roared, with a tone of satisfaction in his voice, and fled to the back entry with his moronic followers, the racket subsiding more and more. Smithy gave me a leg over the hedge, and I was met by groans of pain.

"My arm's broken Tod, I can't move it," he moaned.

By the time the ambulance had arrived the other three had joined us, shocked by the events and swearing revenge on Woodland, which deep down I knew would never happen, especially as it was headed by an individual who was mentally deranged.

"Once I've done my basic training, Rammy's gonna get it!" scowled Diesel.

"You better believe it!" added Gazzer.

"Who's going to tell his mum?" asked Larry. It was a good question. I made my way to his house with Smithy.

CHAPTER THREE

'The reservoir'

In the summer of '82, before the incident with Rammy, we had spent a lot of time at the reservoir just off Clough Lane which was commonly known as the Raz. We had just finished our fourth year at school and had plenty of time on our hands. On this particular day, after many outings there, we met at around ten with our towels slung over our backs, except Chad, of course, who had his designer towel rolled up and proudly held at his side whilst his doting girlfriend puffed on a cigarette. How cute!

While we were waiting for Larry, Smithy explained how his new computer programme worked. He claimed that it was faster and more effective than any other programme he had created. I glanced at Diesel and Gazzer, as his pupils seemed to protrude through his jam jar glasses, and it was very clear that smirks were beginning to appear on their faces. The smirks turned into smiles and yes, the smiles turned into laughter. Stopped in his tracks, Smithy asked what was funny and then started to head to the Raz on his own.

"Come on, Smithy!" cried Diesel.

"Only messing!" shouted Gazzer, at which point all three of them engaged in a towel fight accompanied by lots of insults and laughter.

When Larry did finally arrive, we asked why he was so late, to which he replied, "Had to feed Snowflake, sorry lads. "I could see that Murph was on the brink of making a joke about a horse and a glue factory and quickly interjected with "Right, shall we go?" I wanted to go swimming today without everybody arguing. The sun was beating down and when we arrived at the Raz, the water looked so inviting. The frame of an old mining shaft jutted through the surface of the water and we used this for diving. It was known as the Plough.

It goes without saying that there is no show without Punch, and Gazzer and Diesel were doing somersaults and turns from the Plough without too much effort.

"Let's have a dive Larry!" shouted Gazzer. "You've not been on the Plough this summer!"

I looked at Larry and he seemed nervous but tried to disguise his anxiety with a forced smile.

"OK Gaz!" he replied, "be there in a sec!"

Spindly in stature, he stumbled to the edge of the reservoir bank and swam to the Plough, met by the two lads who helped him up to the diving point of the wooden frame. Diesel giggled, "Do you know what to do?" Larry nodded his head, adding, "Yeah, a piece of cake. "I noticed Smithy nudging Chad with a look of concern on his face. Even Murph looked uncertain of what was going on. I felt a strange feeling in my gut.

Larry took the position for the dive and, almost in slow motion, attempted the somersault, trying to copy that of Diesel and Gazzer. However, he could not execute the dive and lost control, hitting his head on the side of the Plough. He was out for the count and started to sink almost immediately.

My head turned quickly to Diesel. He had clearly frozen. Gazzer tapped him on the arm but there was no response. "Do something, Gaz!" yelled Chad. "For crying out loud, do something!" Suzy started sobbing. Smithy ran to the bank, barking out instructions. Gazzer dived in and grabbed hold of

Larry. I jumped into the water and swam to the site. Together, Gazzer and I secured Larry, making sure his chin was above the water and accelerated to the bank. Chad and Murph pulled him out and Smithy immediately started to pump his chest. Water propelled from Larry's mouth. His eyes were glazed – I feared the worst. . .

Without warning, Smithy gave Larry the kiss of life, trying desperately to get air into his failing lungs. Time was standing still. . . the sun beat down oppressively, and I had an image of Larry's mother at the door, unaware of what had happened. . . The last droplets of water fell out of Larry's mouth and suddenly his chest started to move. Smithy gently rubbed his palms on his chest and slowly but surely Larry started to breathe again. Time gradually resumed its normal pace as we left Larry on the bank to recover.

It had been a sobering moment, to say the least, and we all agreed to never tell Larry how close he was to dying. We simply said that he hit his head against the Plough and Diesel and Gazzer pulled him back to the reservoir bank. It was never mentioned again.

CHAPTER FOUR

'The trip to the moss'

As we know, after Murph's encounter with Rammy, he had plenty of excuses not to go to school. It is true that the moron from Woodland had broken his arm, which was no fault of his own, but Murph did milk the unfortunate event to the hilt, it must be said. His usual retort was, "Well I finish school next year anyway so what difference does it make?" Murph had always been a forward thinker!

He often tried to persuade us to 'wag' a day off school to spend the day with him, claiming that there were more interesting things to do in life than schoolwork. This, indeed, was true but we were not sure that our future employers would entirely agree with this. That said, some of the crew, myself included, I must admit, did have the odd day off without a sick note and headed off to the Moss on Diesel's crosser bike. The Moss was a stretch of waste land just off the Manchester Liverpool road.

On this particular day, in spring, '83, Murph, Diesel, Gazzer and I met at the Wall as others were starting their maths lessons! Diesel and Gazzer had got the fuel for the crosser the night before. This involved visiting cars without a lock on the petrol cap, of course, and syphoning fuel out of them. Diesel would always claim that he might take the occasional litre of diesel fuel without a receipt but that he was not a vandal. It was one saving grace, I suppose.

Gazzer and I walked to the Moss and Diesel gave Murph a ride on the back of the bike. Obviously, he would have had trouble steering it in his present condition. We all eventually joined up at the slag heap on the Moss and started our day of fun at the expense of our teachers. That said, they were probably happier that we were not there. Murph did not really figure in the equation as he was hardly present, but Diesel could get a bit lively in class at times and did spend one or two lesson periods slumped against the wall outside in the corridor. Gazzer was no saint either and did not exactly toe the line in class all the time. However, in metal work he was the top pupil and often praised by his teacher, Mr Ruffle, the only teacher Gazzer got on with.

The slag heaps were dark grey in colour and that day a little damp as it had been raining the night prior.

"Give us a go, Diesel!" said Gazzer.

"OK," Diesel replied, "but don't wreck it, it's slippery today. "

The latter handed the bike to Gazzer. "Mind that chain!" he added "Get your foot stuck in that and you'll be joining Murph on the hospital visits, if you still have a foot left, that is!"

Gazzer climbed onto the crosser and revved the engine. He smiled, looking at the handlebars, and put the bike into first. Up and down the slag heaps the crosser roared, leaving thick track marks in the damp stone behind it.

"Not a bad rider," I commented.

"If my arm was a hundred percent, I'd probably get round quicker than that," murmured Murph.

"Really?" exclaimed Diesel. "Obviously been practising because last summer you weren't exactly Barry Sheen was you Murph?"

I smirked at Diesel as Murph stared at the heaps ignoring the comment.

Gazzer returned to the bench where we were standing and rested the bike against it. "Having a go Tod?" he inquired with a challenging tone, to which I nodded. The slag heaps became a sea of grey as I charged up the hills and down again, my hand squeezing the throttle. As I rode, I was in a different world, only reminded of the real one by the choking petrol fumes from the exhaust. No other bikes were about, and I felt that I could do as I pleased. So liberating, so refreshing, so carefree! This bubble suddenly burst, however, when I heard the lads' cries from a distance to come back as I could only assume that somebody else wanted a go. My assumption was correct.

"Thought you were going to spend the whole morning out there!" Diesel laughed. I threw him the keys, still on a high.

"Coming on the back Murph?" asked Diesel, as he slid onto the seat.

"My arm's bugging me at the moment," he replied. "Maybe later. "

"Bad news," responded Diesel, with little sincerity as his mind was obviously elsewhere. "Right then," he continued, "catch you in a while crocodiles!" and off he sped, the engine rattling as he went.

His performance on the bike really did put our efforts to shame. The bike was moving faster, the corners tighter and the mechanics of the machine were totally in tune with its rider. The slag was propelled into the air as Diesel mastered the crosser and all three of us watched in admiration.

This impressive display of expertise, however, was suddenly interrupted by what looked like a brand new white Range Rover, boasting a thick red stripe on its sides and a blue flashing light! Although a great rider, Diesel was not too hot on paperwork and formalities and I'm sure that road tax and insurance had never entered his head for the crosser. . . The pursuit was underway.

We kneeled behind the bench . Diesel had clearly seen the police car as the bike was now going at full speed on the heaps, to which the Range Rover responded accordingly.

"How is he going to get out of this one?" gasped Gazzer.

"He usually does," responded Murph in an unconvincing manner. We continued to watch.

Diesel knew this area like the back of his hand, and I noticed that he was heading towards the slag hill steps at the other side of the Moss. The formation of the slag was in steps like a staircase with a narrow gap between each one. The bike roared to the steps followed by the ever-attentive police car. Diesel was zig zagging on the slag, almost teasing the police, and before entering a gap on the formation, he turned round and duly showed two fingers to the occupants of the car.

We burst into laughter, but this was curtailed somewhat when the Range Rover put on its breaks and skidded into the slag damaging the right wing of the car. We did not want any harm to come to the driver and his buddy, obviously.

The steps led onto a dirt track which eventually found a main road. Presumably, Diesel took this route as we later met up with him at the Wall after scarpering off the Moss, trying desperately to run behind the slag heaps to avoid the eye of the law. However, to be fair, the two coppers probably had more important things to worry about, like explaining the wreckage on the Rover which before the incident, looked like it had just come off the assembly line. The words boss and hot under the collar sprang to mind.

What a day! The others trickled out as the evening went on and Smithy said that if he heard any more, he would bust a gut. Chad commented that he would have probably 'croaked it' with laughter if he had been behind the bench. Larry smiled at the narrative, calling us 'bad boys'. That much was true!

CHAPTER FIVE

'The fishing night out'

As we touched on before, Diesel enjoyed his fishing and, it had to be said, he was good at it. Smithy was excellent at the theory of fishing, often explaining the ratio of lead shot to float and the hook size to the type of fish you wanted to catch, or indeed the type of bait required for each particular breed of fish, but when it came to getting the fish in the keep net, there were some concerns, let us say. When a fish got off his hook or he lost his landing net in the reeds, which did actually happen once, he would look at us through his thick round spectacles, trying to convince us that the fish was at fault and not him. He could make us laugh!

I enjoyed the sport as well, possessing an old cane rod that my dad used to have when he was a teenager and a secondhand Dunlop reel which I bought with the money from my weekend job as a caddy in the local golf course. My tin contained a small bag of hooks and three floats which had been used so many times that the paint on them had more or less faded! However, as Diesel commented, if you could fish, you could catch a tench with a roll of cotton and to be fair, I was not bad at the sport.

Chad, of course, had all the latest equipment- a brand new split cane rod and an Abu reel which unravelled from the centre, a posh chair and a top of the range fishing basket. When he went fishing, Suzy would sit next to him on her recently purchased deck chair which was cushioned, needless to say. Blowing circles of smoke from her cigarette, she would laugh at Chad's jokes as he watched for his float to go under the water. Much in love, so sweet!

Larry also took an interest in fishing. He had a decent bit of kit and was not bad at it. He did not, however, really take part in the jinks when we had a fishing day. He seemed to be more bothered about catching his fish. Dedication, a great attitude!

It was the end of August '82 or thereabouts and the five of us had decided to do an 'all nighter' on Harp Street Lodge over the way from Cromson street. We gathered at the Black Wall around 6pm, on the Saturday evening, armed with our fishing gear and excited at the prospect of catching a huge tench or a razor teethed pike. Smithy had brought an interesting book on the facts and figures of the greatest fish ever caught and Chad was demonstrating how his new fishing reel worked, not giving fish much of a chance, he claimed.

"Such enthusiasm!" I murmured to Diesel, which was met by a suppressed laugh, not attracting attention as intended.

Larry did not say much as we waited to go. He just sat on his fishing basket looking in the direction of Clough Farm where Snowflake's stables were located, of course.

We all trundled to Harp Lodge after the banter at the Wall and eventually started to fish around eightish. Smithy was the first to cast his float, as you would expect, and the rest followed. Diesel had brought a bottle of whiskey which soon got passed around the group, and I had four cans of Skol lager which I had lifted out of my dad's cellar. They would be replaced, of course, when I next got paid at the golf course! Suzy soon left after eight, giving Chad a parting kiss and telling him that she would be back in the morning with a flask of coffee and a Penguin biscuit, which she knew he liked. . .

As the night drew in, Larry suddenly got a bob on his float. "It's looking good," he whispered to Chad who was at the side of him. Chad looked on, which, in turn aroused the attention of us all. The float went under the water two or three times. That was enough for Larry. He pulled his rod and it started to bend. The fish took him into the reeds and Larry played it as best he could. He was clearly struggling and Smithy, sensing this, decided to run over to him and take command of his fishing rod.

"You've got to pull the rod from side-to-side Laz," instructed Smithy, saliva forming at the sides of his mouth. I watched in disbelief as Diesel and Chad laughed openly.

At this point, the fish, probably a tench, had won the battle but Smithy continued to fight, letting out line from the reel and explaining why he was doing it. Larry stood there, his mouth wide open, as if a nightmare was unravelling before him and then it happened – the line snapped. We all looked at our rods and continued to fish. It was the start of the night and arguing would have ruined the trip, but this did not excuse Smithy from being a real nerd! Larry put on a new float and cast his line without even saying a word. An incredible event. By the time 2am had arrived, yes, we were all asleep in our deck chairs except Diesel who carried on fishing. Smithy had caught nothing but claimed that he could have reeled in five or six if he had had the rub of the green. Diesel whispered that he had had a rub of something during the night, but it was certainly not the green. I had to snigger; I could not help it. As for the others, Larry brought in a roach around midnight and Chad bagged a fair sized tench just past the hour of 1am. Before dropping off I netted a couple of tench also. I will not go on, at the risk of sounding like Smithy!

It is true that Diesel continued to cast his line until Suzy showed up next morning and I believe he netted four or five. However, he failed to warn us of several rain showers that started after we dozed off and we all woke up on Suzy's arrival soaked to the skin.

"You could have woken us up, Diesel," I said, laughing when I realised that I did not have a dry stitch on me.

"I was so busy laughing, Tod, that I never got round to it!" he replied, watching for any movement in his float.

Chad found it funny but Suzy not so.

"Look at Chad, he's wet through Diesel!" she cried. "You might have said something!"

A smile slowly developed on Diesel's lips as he finished the contents of his whiskey bottle.

"I'm off lads!" shouted Smithy without warning. "A shit night for fishing," he added, water dripping off his jeans and condensation gathering on the lenses of his glasses. Larry took off also, oblivious to being saturated it seemed, his only concern being to get back to the farm and tend to his horse.

To be fair, it had been a bit of a mixed bag, but I would not have changed it for anything. Smithy made a complete nerd of himself, which was hilarious, we had a few drinks, shared a few jokes and caught one or two fish in the process. On the downside, we all walked home like drowned rats. But, hey ho! such is the life of a teenager.

CHAPTER SIX

'The milk round'

Christmas, '82 was approaching and money for presents was scarce, especially since the golfers had recently stopped playing due to the bad weather. "Three more weeks and it'll be the big day," commented Smithy. We all nodded as we leaned against the Wall, condensation appearing at every breath.

"Yeah, I could do with a bit of cash," I answered. "Haven't got a dime for Christmas. "

"You could always help at the farm if you want," suggested Larry. "Old Darcy always needs a bit of help at this time of the year with milk, cream and all that. "

"Any room for another one, Larry?" asked Smithy. "Going a bit short myself at the moment. "

"I can always ask the old man," responded Larry. "He is really busy for the next two or three weeks. "

Darcy had a horse and cart from which he delivered milk and other things all around the Raz and even farther afield. Larry had helped him since starting secondary school in return for a few quid and the opportunity to ride Snow Flake.

"You don't need a milk round, do you Chad?" joked Diesel.

"Don't know Diese," laughed Chad. "Suzy has a very expensive lifestyle. You might want to ask Darcy if there's any space for another one Laz!"

We all laughed except for Suzy, of course, who was more interested in giving Chad a most dirty look that would blow him out of the water if, indeed, he was a ship!

Diesel and Gazzer took part in the conversation, needless to say, but they were more drawn to motor bikes, as you may imagine, and they left early that night as they were on the crosser next morning and needed to find a few 'suitable' cars accompanied by a long tube and an empty coke bottle. Murph was clearly out of the frame as regards the job because of his arm. In fact, before leaving, Gazzer had commented that Darcy would have to give him half pay if he ever worked on the cart. We laughed. . .

Larry appeared at the Wall one or two days later with good news. He had spoken to Darcy, who said that Smithy and I could help out in the run up to Christmas on the cart. We would be given one pound fifty each day from four in the morning to seven thirty, and on Friday morning, at the end of the shift, we got a warm cup of coffee and one of Mrs Darcy's cream cakes at the farmhouse. Larry mentioned that we were not needed at the weekend because Darcy's nephew helped out on those days. Seven pounds fifty a week, however, would be very useful and what is more, I had not had a cream cake for ages. Smithy was over the moon with the wage. I just hoped that he would not send us all to sleep, It was early enough in the morning as it was!

Monday morning soon arrived, together with the snow. Fortunately, we had broken up for our Christmas holidays. It was almost four in the morning and Larry, Smithy, and I were stood outside the farmhouse waiting for Mr Darcy to appear. At four on the dot, the front door opened, and the old man pointed to the yard where the horse and cart were ready to go, loaded to the brim with cream, milk, and heaven knows whatever else! We followed him, the snow crunching beneath our feet and the freezing air filling our lungs. It was our first day and we were not exactly sure what to do, but as the morning progressed things became a little clearer.

We were basically Darcy's runners. He would stop the horse and shout out what each house wanted. Halfway through the round in Gladstone Road, Smithy had what can only be described as a mishap. Darcy yelled out the order and Smithy ran to the door with four cartons of milk, two in each hand, but did not see the step because of the snow and went flying on his back . It was comical, even Larry laughed as he went to help him. "Alright Smithy?" he asked. "Let me help you up!"

"Cheers Laz. "The words trundled out of Smithy's mouth and I could not help thinking about the incident at the Raz five or six months earlier, when Larry nearly died. He never knew that Smithy had saved his life as we had vowed never to mention it, but now the tables had turned and he was helping Smithy in times of trouble, albeit on a lesser scale.

It was so touching, and for once I am being sincere when I say this.

Darcy had no time for passengers. He told Smithy to get back in the cart and snapped on the reins to the next street.

Towards the end of the round, we finally had a chance to have a chat as the final streets were at the bottom of Clough Lane. Smithy started talking about a girl he fancied in his year, Laura Simpson. Larry and I both knew of Laura as we were all in the same year at school. "When I'm talking to her, she doesn't half get me going," he said. "Shaped like a peach!" He had obviously fully recovered from his fall.

"Yes, she's fit Smithy but do you think you have a chance with her? She sees Jacko now and again. Do you think she'll find time for you as well?" I responded.

Jacko was the cock of the year and I'm sure that if Smithy tried anything with Laura Simpson, he would be launched to Mars and back. I did not say this, of course, as I did not want to hurt the lad's feelings.

I found it a little strange that Larry did not have much to say about this on the cart. All the lads fancied Laura Simpson and when I asked him if he would give it a go, he simply nudged Darcy, pointing him in the right direction for the final drops, as the farmer had been complaining that everything looked the same in the blanket of snow. After delivering about twenty pints to the last street, we headed back to the farm. The snow glistened under the streetlamps and the cold air stung our cheeks. I had a great feeling of achievement after earning my first day's wage and I walked out of the farmyard very content. Smithy was talking about the new computer that he was saving up for on the way home. I simply humoured him because to be truthful, I did not care about new computers, but I felt good because I had finished my shift on the cart, and this obliterated Smithy's tedious narrative. Larry spoke a little about Darcy's horse before saying goodbye at the top of Clough Lane where he lived.

CHAPTER SEVEN

'Break dance'

It was late spring in that wonderful year of '82 and the end of the fourth year at school was in sight. Break dance had been the 'in thing' that year, of course. The Black Wall always kept in touch with what was in vogue.

We often practised in the field facing the Wall armed with an old piece of card that Chad had kindly donated from the box of his new racing bike and Gazzer's ghetto blaster.

On this specific day, we all met at the Wall at roughly ten o'clock. It was a warm Saturday morning, and everyone was in good spirits. Gazzer was the chief at break dance and wore his old, tired Adidas track suit and Mamba trainers. It was true that Chad sported a brand-new track suit and bottoms but, if given the choice, I'm sure that the rest of us would have taken the Adidas because it was being worn by 'the master'. Suzy continuously touched Chad's track suit top admiringly as she chit chatted with him, which Diesel and I thought was so sweet, they were such a nice couple. . .

"Nice hat!" shouted Murph to Diesel.

"Cheers, Murph," answered Diesel whilst proudly fingering his recently acquired cap. He wore a red 'tracky' with a white stripe through it. Although accomplished in his break dancing, he was not quite to the standard of Gazzer, which he knew, but endeavoured to equal or even surpass it by training as much as he could.

Smithy was not at all bad at the old six step which I am saying incidentally, not him for a change! He chatted in his sportswear with Larry who was lent against the Wall in the track suit he used for his milk round at Clough Farm. He struggled on some of the moves, like the windmill and the caterpillar, but when performing in the group this was always overlooked.

Murph was obviously fashion correspondent for the day, this time taking an interest in my attire. "Where did you get the tracky, Tod?" he asked. "Is it new?" he continued.

"Got it a couple of weeks ago, in town," I replied. "It was in the sales. " Not that my parents had given me any money for it because they did not have any! I had saved it up from my golf job, which I think has been mentioned before.

"Where did you get yours Murph?" I joked, "at a jumble sale?" This comment provoked much amusement and Murph, a little red in the face, it must be said, turned up Gazzer's ghetto blaster, which was playing music from the band East Avenue Mob.

"He's only joking," said Suzy, grinning, to which Murph did the same.

Believe it or not, we did actually have a plan for that day, which was unusual for us. The idea was to practise break dance on the field for a few hours and then make our way to the social club of Diesel's dad, whose friend was retiring from a prison in Manchester and having a retirement lunch and dinner there. He had been a prison officer and a good friend of Diesel's dad for a long time and we had been invited to do a break dance show for an hour or so. There was going to be a bucket passed around, so they story went, which, between seven of us might bring in a tidy sum!

Music, by East Avenue Mob, blared from Gazzer's ghetto blaster on the field and everyone went through their moves. The cardboard creased and stretched as Gazzer and Diesel did their windmills and I did the caterpillar together with Chad and Murph. Larry and Smithy did an impressive crab walk and all together we looked pretty good, If I say so myself. Suzy had invited three of her friends who were going to the social club with us. They watched with fascination on their faces.

The girls were called Petra, Yvonne, and Wendy. Petra was truly pretty and came over to the UK from Malawi with her mother and father in the early seventies, as her father had got a job as a doctor in Manchester. Yvonne, although pleasant enough, had a reputation of being a bit of a girl and liked the lads, although, I'm sure Suzy would have objected to this comment. Wendy, also, was not far behind Yvonne on the boys' scene, so the word was on the street, albeit nice in character as the other two were.

The practice went really well and sweat pumped out of our faces, accompanied by smiles of contentment, which found their way to Suzy's giggling friends who were sat on pieces of cardboard not far away. I wondered if anything else was on the agenda besides break dance that day.

Needless to say, some of us did not have the money for bus fare to get to the social club and Smithy, Gazzer, Diesel, Murph and I took old day passes, hoping that the bus driver would not check the dates. Chad obviously had his bus fare, and so did Larry and they got on the bus first with the four girls who had also brought some money. The driver, occupied by those who were paying, did not take much notice of the dates on the old tickets as we slid past the others. He just nodded his head, to our relief, otherwise it would have been a long walk!

When we arrived at the social club, the guests had just finished their lunch and some were rather worse for wear. Diesel's dad greeted his son. "Hi Tez, a lot of them have had one or two at lunch time, so you'll probably get a bit of cash," he laughed. "Make sure you've got a big bucket. . . a few spectators, Tez?" He pointed at the girls and then smiled at Diesel with a glint in his eye, which his son reciprocated.

"Coffin dodgers, Tod," Murph observed. "Half of them will probably have a heart attack when the ghetto blaster starts, "he laughed. Another shrewd and sensitive comment from a friend whose opinion I valued highly.

After an enthusiastic introduction from Diesel's dad on the microphone, Gazzer turned on the blaster and the East Avenue Mob filled the room. Gazzer came into his own. He started with the salsa step and then went into the kick and twist, followed by a very convincing chair freeze and jack hammer. After doing an Indian step, Diesel indulged in a most impressive caterpillar whilst I was doing a hand hop preceded by a pretty good hustle step. The others were also doing a good show, but whilst I was dancing, I noticed that Suzy's friends were burning holes through the tops of the three of us with their stares and apparent admiration.

The finale of the event was superb. Gazzer spun on his head for about thirty seconds as the six of us did a hand glide freeze in a circle around him and the guests in the room roared with appreciation, throwing coins and notes into the bucket which was flying around the room. Gazzer suddenly went into a role and got to his feet receiving a rapture of applause. The show had been a great success and I was curious, as I'm sure the others were, as to how much the bucket had raised.

We wiped our dripping brows and after chatting with the now ex prison officer and Diesel's dad, we left the club around four thirty to catch our bus home which this time we could all pay for!

Gazzer, Diesel, and I counted the money on the back seat of the bus, and I noticed again that Petra, Yvonne, and Wendy were paying us special attention, laughing and giggling as the coins jingled around. Diesel and Gazzer clearly picked up on it too as they nudged each other and then nudged me whilst the girls were temporarily distracted by something through the window. "It's the haystack tonight," whispered Gazzer, to which we both nodded back with a smirk.

We got off the bus and made our way to the Wall. We had made approximately sixty-two pounds, which was shared between the seven of us.

"Buying us a beer?" asked Wendy looking at Diesel with a giggle.

"You never know your luck," he laughed. "There is an off licence round the corner. Fancy a walk with me, Gazzer and Tod?" he inquired.

"Only if Petra and Yvonne can come," answered Wendy.

"Yeah, that would be nice, wouldn't it Petra?" interjected Yvonne, glancing at Gazzer. It was as if they had already decided what and who they wanted.

Not wasting time, I grabbed Petra's hand and we started walking. "See you soon Suzy," Petra shouted, which was received with a little wave. The look on the faces of Smithy and Murph was quite a picture. Envy showed a great presence, together with frustration and a little surprise, I think. So sweet that they took an interest in my welfare! Chad winked as I walked past and Larry said thanks for a good day, rattling the coins in his pocket.

Diesel, Wendy, Gazzer and Yvonne met me and Petra outside the off licence and I went in, after taking some money from the lads. In those days, getting served was not a problem and I left the shop with eight cans of beer and a couple of bottles of whiskey.

"How does a walk to the haystacks grab you Yvonne?" smirked Gazzer.

"Only if Petra and Wendy come," she giggled. The other two girls laughed and the stroll to Farmer Darcy's haystack began.

I found Petra really pretty and on the way to the farm we spoke about the school she went to and talked about her days in Malawi. We laughed and joked, just as the other two couples did and time flew by. We made our way to Darcy's place. We had spoken about Larry's horse on the way to the girls and Petra especially was keen to see it, which she did, as the mare was still grazing when we arrived. "A beautiful horse," she commented.

It was eightish and still light as we ran to the hay shed, keeping an eye out for old Darcy. We divided the contents of the bag and found comfortable places in the stack where we could enjoy our booty, each couple having their private space, needless to say.

I became unaware of Diesel and Gazzer at this point as I wanted to concentrate on Petra, and I think she welcomed this attention. We cracked open a can of beer. "You don't think that I'm easy, do you Tod?" she asked and, shaking my head, I leant over and kissed her. One thing led to another and before we knew it, we were making love on the hay. The break dancing had been exhilarating, that much is true, but it did not come anywhere near my time with Petra and hopefully she thought the same.

At around ten, she said that she had to go, and we walked to a telephone box where I called her a taxi. I never saw her again as Suzy told me that she would have easily become serious with me but her father forbade any distractions in her studies and that included boys. I was so upset. So much. . .

CHAPTER EIGHT

'Last weekend before class -Take one'

It was the beginning of September '82 and Smithy's nerdish behaviour at Harp Lodge had been long forgotten. We even laugh about that today when we meet. What a tool, don't you think?

The start of fifth year was on the horizon and we decided to go to town, as it were, the weekend before it started. The summer 'blow out', as it was termed, was going to have one or two incidents, I was sure of that and indeed, I was not mistaken.

We all met at the Wall at sixish, laughing and joking as we looked forward to what the weekend had to offer. The money from the break dance had long gone but we scratched together enough coins to get two bottles of whiskey from the off licence and a large bar of fruit and nut. Larry's mum and dad were flying out to Greece that night and the house would be free from around nine o'clock, so a party was planned for later in the evening. Apparently, Larry had stocked up with a crate of lager for the gathering, which we thought was pretty damned decent of him. Diesel and Gazzer had invited Wendy and Yvonne from the show at the social club, as you may remember, and the word was that they were supposed to be bringing a few of their mates. Petra would not be there, but the fact that Wendy and Yvonne were going gave me a distant hope, but one that I realised would never materialise.

I had not seen the two girls since the night at the haystacks in spring but I heard stories throughout the year of Diesel and Gazzer taking them to Darcy's place for a bit of 'rough and tumble' ,as the lads put it, without the need of much persuasion from them!

"What are we going to do until the party?" piped up Murph, swigging from the whiskey bottle. He had a point, for once!

"We could pay a visit to 'Johnny-know-it-all', "laughed Gazzer. "I'm sure he would appreciate a visit!"

We all sniggered. When we were larking about on the street playing hare and hounds or just being loud, 'Johnny-know-it-all' would come out and give us a lecture on civility and acceptable behaviour. He would remind us that when he was a teenager, he was a bit of a lad and as boisterous as we were, but he always knew the limit. That was something that the Crommy Boys failed to comprehend.

He would often give us the examples of when he was fighting the cock of the neighbouring school in the street where he lived, doing it quietly so as not to upset the residents, or when he was having a bit of 'slap and tickle' with one of the local girls he would do it at the back of the mission building so that the people of the street would not be offended by it! All of which was total hog wash. He probably sat in his bedroom all night with his books and whatever else he got up to.

The whiskey had started to take effect and I could see a devilish look in Diesel's eyes. "How about a moony lads?" he cried. "A good moon shine for our friend Johnny. "Smithy, Gazzer, Murph, myself and obviously Diesel were up for it, but Larry decided that he would nip home to see his parents before they left, and then meet us later at the house as planned. Chad said that he had to go to Suzy's place to pick her up for the party. Everyone to their own. The five of us left, set up a plan. Gazzer would knock on Johnny's while the other four waited outside his wall. On opening the door, Johnny would see Diesel's moon shine and be scarred for life or collapse in shock.

The latter certainly did not happen as Johnny, seeing Diesel's arse, quickly put his shoes on and bolted after us! Diesel was still pulling his pants up as he ran away with the rest of us. Totally hilarious. The night had definitely begun with a bang! We fled down the back entry and Johnny, although not an invalid, was no spring chicken either and we got away, ending up halfway to town.

"That was such a laugh!" howled Gazzer, to which Diesel replied, "Probably the funniest thing this week!"

"He can still move though," murmured Smithy, catching his breath, as we returned back to the Wall.

"We'll have to make sure he doesn't see us again tonight," noted Murph, who always had good points to offer. That thought never would have occurred to me!

There was still a little time to burn before the party and we had brought out an old coin, which resembled a ten pence piece with a hole drilled in the middle. Through the hole I had fed some cat gut, which was lying around in my fishing basket. Ideal for pranks, now was the time for its entrance.

"What do you think lads?" I laughed, on our arrival back to the Wall, swinging the coin from the cat gut. Gazzer grabbed it off me, smirking. We had played this little game before and he knew exactly what to do. The two whisky bottles were almost drained as we made our way to the mouth of the back entry leading into Clough Lane, which always had people on it.

Hiding behind the wall of the entry, Gazzer flipped the coin on the pavement and it was not long before we got a bite. A middle-aged man spotted it and bent down to pick it up. Of course, Gazzer pulled on the line and the bloke tried to follow it, falling flat on his face. This was met by a very unsympathetic guffaw. We fled down the entry with our new friend in pursuit. "You little cretins!" was his cry as he sprinted after us but, thankfully, after a minute or so his threatening silhouette disappeared, and we returned to our original hiding place from where we had been rudely dispatched.

Our next victims were a couple in their thirties. We saw the woman pointing to the coin, to which the bloke nodded and subsequently bent down to pick it up. He also followed the bait but this time he went flying into the garden wall in front of him and head butted the brick work. Talk about laugh, we could not stand up ourselves! However, we soon sobered up when he got up and, although dazed, managed to force a sprint in our direction. His girlfriend screamed "Leave it Tony!" as she followed after him and, quickly turning around, I saw the two of them racing down the cobbled alley.

"Take a left onto the field!" shouted Diesel and, grabbing hold of Smithy, who was lagging a little, we escaped by the car garages just off the field. Our hearts pumping and perspiration falling off our brows, we remained hidden until the coast was clear.

"He could have caused us a few problems if he had got hold of us," Murph sharply commented. I'm sure that tea and biscuits would not have been on the agenda.

The clock hand was approaching nine and we decided to head off to Larry's place. Being sobered up by the recent activity, albeit an absolute hoot, a few cans of lager would be most welcome.

We knocked on the door and Larry opened it. Music blared in the background. "Welcome to the house of fun!" grinned Chad, with Suzy on his arm. Yvonne and Wendy giggled on the sofa as the five of us entered. I did not see any other of Suzy's friends, however.

"Hi boys!" giggled Yvonne again, "A nice night for Darcy's hay shed. Larry tells me it's just around the corner!" she added, putting on a little more lip stick.

"Surely there's somewhere else to go, the house is empty," laughed Gazzer.

Chad had brought another crate of lager and by half ten the whole lot of us were steaming. Whilst dancing to music that had become a bit of a blur, people started to fall over each other, which everyone found most amusing. Murph even tried his luck with Wendy at one point, who probably would have gone for it, but for Diesel being there. He did not look too concerned when he saw what was going on. He thought it was quite funny, in fact. The whole evening had been a scream and it was not over yet. Around elevenish we picked up Larry's phone and called the taxis.

We were not thinking straight, and, on reflection, we should not have sent them to the house of 'Johnny-know-it-all' because, to be fair, we had already shown him a moony that night. It was nothing to be proud of but, at the time, it was extremely funny.

Smithy, Gazzer and Yvonne called six taxis between them, to arrive in the next half hour at

Johnny's place. This gave us enough time, after having a lager, of course, to get to the house and find a good hiding place from which to observe the goings on. Chad commented on the way there that we were mental, and he was not far wrong, not after the amount we had drunk, at any rate. Smithy, Gazzer, Yvonne, Diesel, Wendy, Murph, Larry, Chad, Suzy and I squeezed behind the top garage off the field that looked onto Cromson Street and Johnny's house. We kept well away from the Wall because that would be the first place that Johnny boy would look for us.

Two taxis appeared together, then a third and almost immediately afterwards the other three rolled up. One of the taxi drivers knocked on Johnny's door and he came to the pavement to talk to them all in full view. He was waving his arms, looking around and looking most agitated. We tried to suppress our laughter, but it was very difficult and, at one point, I thought that he might hear us, but he was so busy talking to the taxi drivers that he missed the outbursts from behind the garage.

Eventually, the taxis moved off, one by one, and the last driver even shouted an obscenity at Johnny through the window, which provoked a shake of the fist from him, adding even more hilarity to the event. How we walked back to Larry's, I'll never know because our guts were hurting and that, together with the alcohol made the process almost impossible. "I don't want this night to end!" cried Wendy to Diesel, who just laughed uncontrollably.

"You won't get better than this Wend," he replied, "and there's more to come when we get back!" Wendy giggled and grabbed his hand.

Once back, we all tried to find somewhere to sleep for the night. I am not sure that Larry was aware that we were all decking down for the night at his place, especially as he would be going out to do his milk round at four in the morning and, in effect, leave the control of the building in our less than capable hands. However, the dye had been cast and there was no going back now.

Gazzer, Yvonne, Diesel and Wendy got the bedrooms which, I am sure, were put to good use and Larry had his own bedroom. Whether he got any sleep or not is a different matter. I managed to get one of the sofas and before nodding off, Petra entered my head for a moment, and I could see her laughing in the hay shed. I couldn't help shedding a tear. I hope you do not mind me sharing that with you, a bit silly, I know.

CHAPTER NINE

'Last weekend before class – Take two'

I heard Larry leaving the house early but soon drifted back to sleep, only to be awoken by Smithy around eight o'clock, bleeping on his pocket computer game, which he took everywhere with him.

"Cracking night last night wasn't it, Tod?" he said, carrying on with his game.

"Priceless," I replied, slowly coming round. "I was laughing that much that I could hardly stand up. A bit harsh on Johnny though."

"Yeah, I suppose, but he's such a tool, Tod," he muttered, as he tapped away on the screen. That much was true, but I could not help feeling a little guilty for the double whammy that Johnny had been put through in the name of humour. He would get over it, I was sure. He had in the past.

"Alright lads!" shouted Gazzer, as he burst through the lounge door. "Heard you talking, has Larry got any milk? Yvonne wants a coffee," he asked.

"There's a carton on the bottom shelf," replied Murph, whom we could just about make out under a couple of coats and an old towel.

"Cheers, Murph," responded Gazzer, and skipped into the kitchen, putting on the kettle.

"Someone's in good spirits this morning!" shouted Smithy, directing his voice towards the kitchen.

"Too right Smithy, you want to try it sometime!" replied Gazzer.

Murph and I laughed but my stomach was still hurting from the previous night, and I found it difficult to carry on for more than a few seconds.

"Anyone seen Chad?" continued Gazzer, as he looked for the sugar.

"They must have gone early Gaz. You know what he's like. Doesn't hang around," I replied.

Murph held his head, obviously suffering from the night's excesses, inquiring about the day's plan of action. I had not given it any thought, to be fair, but it was a good point. We would not spend the rest of the day in Larry's house which, I am sure, he would not be too keen on anyway! We had to get out.

As I thought of possible activities for the day, I heard a key turning in the door.

"Alright Laz!" yelled Murph.

Smithy and I nodded to Larry as he reclaimed part of the sofa that Smithy had used during the night.

"Fancy a barbeque in the woods Laz? Set a fire going and sober up a bit maybe?" I suggested.

"Don't see any reason why not," he replied. "There are some sausages in the freezer, and we can always take a few eggs from the old boy's chicken coop. I'm sure he won't miss them. "

"My mum's got some bread that's going out of date," interjected Smithy. "We can make some French bread. "

So, a sketch of the day's events was beginning to appear and it seemed to be welcomed by all the rest of the crew. When Diesel and Wendy finally surfaced, they gave the idea a big thumbs up and Yvonne pointed out that she did not like barbeques without brown sauce, so Gazzer and herself would nip to the off licence to get a bottle and meet up with the rest of us at the Wall later on. Larry and Murph had relieved Darcy of a dozen eggs without the hens realising, never mind the farmer, and Smithy had raided his mum's pantry, holding an old carrier bag containing two loaves. Together with the box of sausages that were now more or less defrosted and a bit of cooking oil, we were all ready for the expedition into the woods. I think that we needed some fresh air and to mend after the escapades of the night before.

As we headed out, Chad put his head out of the upstairs window which looked onto Cromson Street and asked us where we were going. He seemed to like the idea and said that he and Suzy would bring three or four cans of beans for the fry up, which went down well with everybody. He knew where we built the fire. We had done it many times before in the past.

As always, when going to the woods, we could not cut through Wood Oak Fields because that was where the Woodland crew gathered and, as we have touched on earlier, the gang had one or two unsavoury characters within its ranks. Entering it from the main road, we had to walk down a narrow path on a slope, which normally was a simple process, but it proved to be a little challenging today for a few of them who were still recovering from the previous night. Murph slipped and fell on his behind and Smithy tripped over a step and went flying into Diesel, who laughed it off, commenting that he was a spanner. He was a spanner at times. The observation was correct.

The site for the fire was near a tree swing, a slag heap which we slid down on a car bonnet and an aerial runway which had been there for years and ran over the stream. We would simply get up and do something when the conversation was running a bit thin.

The early flames appearing from the kindling wood, grew bigger in size and eventually large branches and old chunks of wood lying around, were being thrown onto the fire. The pan and plates, which had been kindly lent by Larry's parents, unbeknown to them, of course, were brought out and within ten minutes the sausages were sizzling away under the watchful eye of Smithy who, despite comments made earlier, was a good cook. Again, my words, not his!

Gazzer salivated as Smithy started to dish out the sausages and, after adding a fair amount from the sauce bottle, he shovelled three of them down before I even had time to cut into my first.

"He's a hungry lad," giggled Yvonne. "All that activity last night. "

From the look on everyone's faces, we were not sure whether she was referring to the activity in Cromson Street the night before or the activity in Larry's parents' bedroom in the early hours of that morning. After a quick scan of the information available, I concluded that it was a bit of both. Smiles began to appear as we ate our food.

It was true that Smithy was the chef, but he had to eat as well and I grabbed the pan, endeavouring to make French bread. I did not do badly actually. Egg coated slices were distributed to expectant plates surrounding the fire and gobbled up without further ado. Chad and Suzy had arrived by that time and Smithy took over the pan, pouring three cans of beans into it, which Chad had brought. As the tomato sauce bubbled, Diesel offered his plate first. "Think it's this fresh air. It's giving me an appetite," he noted. I was expecting a comment from Wendy but, surprisingly, she was too busy eating her French bread to bother.

"Anyone fancy a game of pinpoint stick?" asked Murph, as the eating was drawing to a close. This involved swinging on the tree rope with a sharp stick and putting it into the ground so as to make it difficult for the next person to pick it up. "I'll start," he continued, sitting on the plank of wood tied to the rope.

"Easy, that," said Chad, watching where Murph had put the stick. He walked to the swing.

"Careful Chad!" shouted Suzy, as she sat on the grass near the tree. "Make sure it doesn't snap. "

Diesel and Gazzer looked at me and I had to cover my mouth with blackened fingers from the charred wood. Luckily, I did not have a mirror in my back pocket.

Chad had no trouble with Murph's pinpoint, just as Diesel had no problem with Chad's attempt. Diesel made it very difficult for the next person however as he did not sit on the seat but hung from it, securing himself with his legs and putting the stick in an almost impossible place to retrieve. It was Smithy's go next. "Better take my glasses off," he joked. "Don't want to break them. "

Good thinking Smithy, I thought, but how would you be able to see properly? I pondered, as he climbed onto the swing and hung his head down, as Diesel had done. He coaxed the rope into getting near the stick and tried three times to grab it, but he missed each time. Frustrated, he tried again, without success.

"Leave it Smithy!" cried Chad. "He can't see," he murmured to me. He was right but, before we could do anything, Smithy stretched a bit too far and fell off the swing tumbling down the slope. It did look comical, but it was only when he got up with just a few bumps and grazes that most of us gave a suppressed snigger, further camouflaged by enquiries about his welfare.

"Alright, Smithy?" asked Chad.

I passed him his glasses. He took them, with a nod of the head, and sat down, his pride clearly dented.

"Leave him for a while," said Gazzer. "He'll come round. "

That is exactly what we did and as we slid down the slag heap on the car bonnet a little later, he walked over and asked for a go. "Give us a go Diesel!" he joked. "You've been on it for ages!"

"Alright," smiled Diesel, "but, this time wear your glasses," and he passed over the bonnet as we all laughed.

Time raced by in the woods, as it often does when you are enjoying yourself. We headed to the aerial runway before making tracks back to the Wall. The runway comprised of a metal wire with a pulley, from which a handle dangled. It was used to get from one side of the stream to the other. There was a knot at the end of the line to stop you going into the tree at the bottom, but the idea was to jump off before you hit the knot to stop yourself from rebounding.

The girls were not too keen on trying the runway out and washed the dishes in the stream instead. Gazzer and Diesel obviously clowned around on it, holding onto the handle with one hand and singing as they went, to create a show for Yvonne and Wendy who were indeed impressed by their tom foolery. They blew kisses to the lads overhead as they washed the plates and giggled to each other constantly. Murph, who was not as athletic as Gazzer or Diesel nor, perhaps, as sharp, decided that he too would give the girls a laugh. You may remember that he did approach Wendy the night before, thinking that he might be in with a chance, which was not the case as long as Diesel was around. He waited in line for his turn, envy and confusion eating into him with every second that passed.

The view looked a little different when you were sliding down a wire, but it was, nevertheless, thrilling and it certainly got my blood flowing. Chad made the journey under the attentive glare of Suzy. He followed her advice to use both hands, to her great relief. Larry did the trip without any problem also.

Murph got on the aerial runway, looking overconfident. He copied Diesel and Gazzer and did the activity using one hand and singing as loud as possible, to get Wendy's attention, who did watch, it had to be said, but not with the same enthusiasm and joy as she did with Diesel. She gave a slight giggle and that was it. However, as far as Murph was concerned he was getting a reaction which distracted him to such a point that he forgot to let go at the bottom of the line and hit the knot. The latter did stop him from hitting the tree, but he heavily rebounded and having only one hand on the handle, he lost his grip and went flying onto the ground without any control at all.

He had been out for the count for about thirty seconds, and by the time we got to him, he was just coming round. He stared at us with glazed eyes. Larry asked him how many fingers he was holding up. Murph answered correctly but he needed time to think before replying. We lifted him up and started the walk back to the Wall. Chad and Gazzer helped him up the narrow path to the main road, along which we strolled to Cromson Street, monitoring Murph all the way.

We chatted at the Wall for a good half an hour and Murph slowly returned to his normal self. I think he realised how pointless his actions had been when he saw Diesel and Wendy hand in hand, lent against the end terrace. He had a sickened look on his face. So much different to when he started the run on the wire.

A bottle of vodka had become available from the spirit cabinet of Larry's dad and we were all invited back for a few shots. The bottle, of course, would be replaced! Not having to be asked twice, we all piled down to Larry's and got merry, talking about the day's events. Even Murph cheered up a little. Some stayed the night, but others went home to at least say hello to their parents before meeting, as we would do, at the Black Wall, the next day.

We had certainly had a final fling before starting fifth year at school and it was a spectacular couple of days, albeit with one or two mishaps, that we would never forget through our last year and probably for the rest of our days.

CHAPTER TEN

'Bonfire night'

The autumn of '82 was upon us. One of the main events of the season for us was Bonfire Night, held on the field opposite the Black Wall. We collected wood each year and all sorts made its way back, including old doors, benches, broken drawers and such like.

This year was no different but, one morning, as Chad was passing the field on the way to the bus stop for school, he made an alarming discovery. All the wood that we had been piling up there had disappeared. When news got to the rest of us, we were obviously vexed but also confused as, the night before, we could see the bonfire wood in its entirety as we talked at the Wall.

We met that night and discussed the mystery. "It's got to be Woodland," suggested Gazzer, chewing on his gum. "They have a bonny every year in the wood," he continued. "They probably dumped it over there."

This comment from Gazzer led to a discussion about all the other gangs in the area who could have carried out the theft. The more names we offered, the more confused we became. As we neared the end of the road without any answer, Larry thankfully plucked an idea out of the air. "Why don't we collect on Thursday and Friday night?" he said. "I'll have a quick look at the field on Friday and Saturday morning and try to catch them at it. Me, Darcy, and his nephew pass it quite a few times on our calls." It was a brilliant suggestion and we all congratulated Larry on the plan, which was set into motion on Thursday evening after school.

We all moved a fair amount of wood to the collection point that night, except for Murph, of course, who had suffered a broken arm a couple of weeks earlier, as you may remember. He followed us, his arm still set in graffiti ridden plaster, reminding everybody of how much wood he had collected last year. He recounted the story of his visit to 'Johnny-know-it-all', which we all know as well as the narrator but it was still funny. He knocked on Johnny's door and asked for firewood, the answer to which was no, but this response came with a usual lecture. Johnny explained to Murph that he was once a teenager himself and enjoyed bonfire night. However, he added that he went to an organised display because a private event, as Johnny put it, was a danger to all. If the fire went out of control it could burn down the residents' fences and gardens and cause absolute mayhem. Murph made an unusually valid point that this could also happen at an organised bonfire, but of course, 'Johnny-know-it-all' had an answer for this, as he always did. Wagging his finger at Murph, who was nearly in a coma at this point, he explained that council displays always had resources at hand for such occurrences, whereas bonfires made by kids had no safety measures, and was, therefore, a perilous activity. As Johnny was reciting various points of health and safely on his soap box, Murph could take no more and left halfway through, to the frustration of the 'fount of knowledge' who told Murph to never call again. He did call again but not for bonfire wood, which you may recall from our get together just before the start of the fifth year.

Both Larry and Chad reported that the timber had not been touched on Friday morning and so there was no need to collect any more for the time being. That evening, whilst looking at the pile from the wall, we were relieved that it was still there but suspected it would not stay for long. "We'll find out who it is" said Diesel with a menacing smile on his face. "When we do, they can put it all back".

That was all well and good, but I wondered what Rammy's reply would be if we asked him to go to the woods and bring back our doors and drawers. The rubber brick was still fresh in our minds and the psychopath was capable of doing much worse than breaking an arm, although I'm sure Murph thought that this was bad enough.

It sounds a little over the top, I know, but I could not sleep very well that night because a thousand formulas passed through my mind and like a failed scientist, I could not come up with a conclusion of who had taken our wood. I eventually nodded off and was woken by a stone on the windows the next morning. I looked out of the window, a little perplexed, as this had never happened before, and I saw Larry standing on the pavement. He signed to open the door which, after throwing on a jumper, I did. I was surprised at what he had to say. "It's the council, Tod," he said anxiously. "They were loading a truck at around half six when I was passing on the cart and they have taken it all, again. "

It never occurred to me that it was the council. I got dressed and walked to the Wall with Larry, chewing on a piece of toast. The others eventually turned up and, although I'm sure they half expected the timber not to be there, this did not stop threats and insults flying out of their mouths. It took a while for this anger to subside, but when things were on a slightly more even keel, I dropped the bomb shell as

I had agreed with Larry. "It's the council, lads. The council are taking the timber. "

Their mouths dropped and they were at a loss to say anything.

"It must be Johnny who called them," piped up Smithy after the hiatus. "He's always been against the bonny. "

It was, indeed, a huge possibility as Johnny's fence bordered the field where the fire was and, as we know, he was very keen to give lectures on health and safety when it came to bonfire night. Of course, we had paid him a visit five or six weeks previously with a moon shine, which would not have helped our cause. Although he had no proof of who had arranged the taxi visit, he probably had a good idea. Why had I not linked him to the incident and why had I not thought of the council? This was a clear misjudgement, and I was somewhat embarrassed.

"Listen lads," I concluded, as desperate to find a solution as they were, "it probably was Johnny, but we don't know it for sure and if we start knocking on his door again, it's going to make the situation worse. We need to tackle the council directly. "

"And how do we do that?" asked Murph, showing me a message to them that he had just written on his plaster.

"By continually collecting wood until the council gets fed up with taking it away," I said, grinning at the comments on his arm. "Just a little each day and when they stop, we can carry more over to the field for the fire itself. "

The days passed by. Each night we threw a little wood on the field and every other day the council truck appeared early morning to collect it. When we suspected that the council was going to turn up, we took turns to wait for them before school. On a couple of occasions, Gazzer distracted the driver whilst Diesel let down one of his tyres, which slowed down the process, and more importantly, made things very uncomfortable for the drivers who came around.

The routine carried on for a couple of weeks until, suddenly, towards the end of October, the council gave up and the timber began to pile up again. If I had been a driver, I would not have wanted to attend here either, listening to nasty comments and insults. What is more the idea of having my tyres let down every other visit would not have appealed to me either.

They were driven out and the lads were happy. Diesel said that he would gather even more wood that year to annoy 'Johnny-know- it-all' and Smithy added that the next time we gave him a visit with a moony, he would do it without reservation.

A day before the big one, we were all sat at the Wall, twiddling our thumbs and staring approvingly at our creation on the field. Any further donations to the fire would be from people visiting it themselves, as we had now finished. "What about a clay fight today?" said Gazzer, without warning. "There's plenty on the back entry near the old electric station, isn't there? We can make a couple of dens in the pile," he continued.

It was a good idea and, besides, there was nothing else to do. We had even sorted out the petrol to start the fire the night before.

We put two shelters together, using old doors and panels from discarded cabinets, and made sure that there was a wide enough space in them to allow us to throw clay at the enemy. There would be three people in each team and Murph would decide who the winners were if there was a stale mate situation, as he could not take part clearly. Gazzer, Smithy and I would be on one team and Diesel, Larry, and Chad would be in the other. Any casualties would be dragged out and sit with Murph.

In our team, Smithy was designated to fetch the clay on a board from the supply point near the electric station when required. Gazzer and I were the foot soldiers but we could, if necessary, call upon our quarter master for support. Larry was their quarter master, and the rules permitted the throwing of clay at either him or Smithy as they left the den to get clay.

The scene was set and soon clay hurtled from one shelter to the other amidst plenty of laughter and name calling. It splattered against the doors and old boards, leaving brown marks everywhere. It was hilarious as Diesel and Chad ducked and dived to avoid the clay and we almost got Larry on several occasions as he dutifully scurried to the electric station to get supplies. They laughed at the same thing, no doubt, as clay whizzed by me and Gazzer, missing us with millimetres to spare. The more clay that Smithy and Larry brought, the more battered the dens looked, and the more tired we became.

It was at this point, all of us being worn out by the battle, that Chad made a serious error. Clay came flying over from Gazzer and myself and Chad, not concentrating for a split second, did not duck and got hit on the chin by a missile. The rules did say that casualties should be dragged out and sit with Murph, but Chad did look in pain, so we called a cease fire and ended the game.

He held his face as he clambered out of the clay-stained den and made his way to the Wall to recover. Fortunately, Suzy was not out that day and Chad, when he eventually started to speak again, said that she should never know, although, the bruise was possibly a bit of a give-away. We later dismantled the pummelled timber and threw it back on the fire pile in preparation for the fifth, which we had devoted three or four weeks of our time to.

It had been worth it, however, and at around six o'clock the next day we all met at the Wall to start the fire. Suzy touched Chad's chin now and then sympathetically as we discussed the plan of action. He had told her that a door had fallen on him as he was throwing it on the pile, which he thought she would accept more than what really happened. He had indeed avoided a lecture, knowing Suzy as we did.

We brought the petrol out of Diesel's garage and brought it to the wood. Under the watchful eye of some of the parents and friends who were there, the fuel was distributed equally on the timber and Gazzer, before striking the match on the petrol ridden rag, whispered, "This is for you Johnny. "The rag spread fire throughout the pile on touchdown and faces lit up with a certain pride, I think it is fair to say.

Diesel's mum baked the potatoes in the fire, as she did every year. She added butter before passing them over in tin foil and they tasted delicious. She also brought a bag of treacle toffee for everyone to share and orange cordial. A nice lady we thought, Diesel's mum, but we only ever got to know her on bonny night.

The field was a mass of colour. The yellow and red flames of the fire merged with the greens, blues and oranges of the fireworks and kids wrote their names, cutting into the darkness with fizzling sparklers. As I contemplated the scene, Chad approached me alone and put his hand on my shoulder, "Miss Petra, do you

Tod?" he said, lighting up one of Suzy's cigarettes, which he did occasionally.

"I do Chad, yes, I do from time to time," I replied, "but her dad did not want it. I can't argue with that."

He looked at the flames as he spoke, "You know, whenever Suzy sees Petra, she speaks of you. She really liked you and says she could have loved you, given the chance. " I nodded, swallowing heavily.

"Come on Tod!" shouted Smithy and Larry, out of the blue. "Murph's got a repeater he's setting off. "

All six of us and Suzy, of course, watched Murph light the firework one handed and the patterns it threw were truly fabulous. As we chatted around the fire, the flames became smaller and people started to drift away, as did the glow and noise of the fireworks.

Bonfire night this year had presented some problems and controversy, but its magnificence tonight and the laughs we had enjoyed in the run up to it, more than made up for the hassle. As midnight drew near, we left the embers to burn themselves out and headed home.

CHAPTER ELEVEN

'A brush with the law'

We were leaving the end of the fifth year and summer was on the horizon. June '83 was a month for revision, as exams were imminent and, although I personally did some, a few of the others were not interested in the finals and had more 'exciting' activities on offer.

Gazzer and Diesel did agree that maths and English were important to get into the marines, but they were of the opinion that these subjects were common sense anyway, and no revision was required. Therefore, their study time could be used for other things, such as improving their agility with physical pursuits, for example hedge hopping, putting two fingers up to the anti-vandalism car and 'narking' at passing cars on the main road, all of which we will touch upon.

Murph's arm had been out of plaster for a while by this time but he had missed a lot of school due to his hospital visits to see the specialist. It is true that he had suffered a nasty fall and there were complications, but he did make a massive meal out of it and skipped classes that he could have attended. It is not surprising, therefore, that the exams barely registered on his agenda for the month. I don't think he even turned up for some of them. He joked that he would write his name on the paper only when he remembered how to spell it!

Needless to say, Murph took a keen interest in Diesel's June undertakings, arm permitting, of course. Smithy, Larry and Chad, on the other hand, were a little more reserved in varying degrees. Smithy enjoyed the mischief on the Street. That goes without saying, but he also liked his computers and facts and figures, as we have seen, and rather than being totally devoted to the June escapades, he took one or two nights out in the week to revise maths and science, which he liked. Larry also liked to be at the Wall, but I seem to remember, at this particular time, he only showed up a couple of times a week because he wanted to be an ambulance driver when he left school and you needed five passes at 'O' Level to do this. He also had to deal with the horse, of course.

We sometimes nick named Chad 'the magician' because he could do a disappearing act at the drop of a hat, if you excuse the pun! You only saw him once or twice a week in June, as he intended to go to the technical college where maths, English and physics were required to get in. Suzy, obviously, encouraged him in his aim to go to college and did not want the boys to be a bad influence on him. She was so selfless, that girl. I would advise anyone to take a leaf out of her book.

I did not make a big deal out of it with the lads, but I was not bad at maths and chemistry at school and after doing a bit at college, I fancied being a chemist of some sort. For that reason, I did a couple of nights' revision a week, as a prospective chemist without his chemistry 'O' Level was not going to get very far! The rest of my time was given to the Street and that month we certainly did have a scream, although we got a little too close to the law on one occasion.

The anti-vandalism car was a good idea from the government, in essence, and certainly our crew never got involved in such activity. However, when its occupants thought that they had elite status in the detective world, armed with a state-of-the-art police car in the pursuit of crime, when, in reality they were two old blokes in an old Ford Fiesta, the discrepancy was a hoot.

One night they were on what they thought was a stake out, observing our behaviour and no doubt preparing to jump over the bonnet to catch us red handed in acts of skull duggery. First of all, it was broad day light, as it was summertime, so the secret surveillance went out of the window, and, secondly, they always parked in the same place so the element of surprise had long gone. Gazzer had brought out a piece of white chalk and an old spray paint canister as he knew that our friends would be waiting around the corner. "Stand behind me , Smithy, with this can," he muttered, "shielding this chalk and my arm so that the old boys can't see anything when I write on the wall. Pretend to be spraying the can. Let's see what happens. "

When the investigators, specially selected of course, saw what we were doing, they burst into action. The doors slammed on the car and the two old timers shouted, "Halt, right there! This is the AVT!" This meant the Anti Vandalism Team. So funny! Gazzer quickly wiped off the chalk with a damp rag in his pocket and, after putting two fingers up to the crusaders, he started to run, followed by the rest of us, except Chad, who was elsewhere that night. Red in the face, our detectives ran back to the Fiesta and started the chase with a rev of the 1. 2 engine.

The brakes of the car screeched as they spun around the corner on our tail. We laughed so much as we ran down the back entry that we could not get any real speed and the two officers of the AVT were catching us up. "Over the railings of the electric station!" shouted Diesel, creased up and struggling to get his words out. As the last person, Murph, hit the shale on the other side, our two buddies skidded along the cobbles of the entry and smashed one of the head lights against the rails. Turning around briefly to view the spectacle, our faces beamed with grins and laughter and this must have put the final nail in the coffin for the AVT squad on duty that night, as the next week they were replaced by two new blokes who proved to be just as comical as the ones we had encouraged to retire, let us say.

While others were revising for their sums and vocab tests, we were having great fun with the 'narking' routine. This involved a team effort, but it was hilarious. Murph and I, for example, would start to point at the drivers' tyres as they passed on the main road. Some of the drivers would stop and wind down the window, at which point, Diesel and Gazzer would shout, 'nark' at them and run off. The reactions were priceless.

An evening in mid-June particularly stands out. We did it to three separate drivers and although the reactions were different, they were equally as funny.

The first car that stopped, politely flashed the head lights before doing so and Smithy, Murph and I ran to the window to 'greet' the driver. Before we had time to warn Gazzer and Diesel that he was a vicar, they both jumped from behind the garden wall where they were hiding and gave the old boy a 'nark' and ran off. We were supposed to run with them, but the vicar looked totally confused and somewhat vacant and, although it brought a smirk to our faces, all three of us knew that there would not be a chase in it and we stayed put, explaining that we did not know who the rogues were who had carried out such a moronic act and we apologised on their behalf.

The expression on the vicar's face changed and he started to grin. "You're all in it together, aren't you?" he laughed. "Tut, tut, should you not be revising for your exams?" he inquired. "That said, I was like you when I was your age, believe it or not. "

Although the vicar's teenage pastimes were tame compared to what we did, we laughed at his stories and warmed to him a little. Not too much as we still had to keep our 'street cred', but the bloke was OK. He became a person rather than a toy that we wound up. A strange experience, we all agreed. This was not, however, the case for the other two cars that we flagged down.

The second car stopped abruptly, and I suspected that this one would be a bit tricky, but this all adds to the hilarity of the evening. A man in his late twenties wound down the window and Smithy, Murph and I ran to the window. He just had enough time to ask, "What's the problem?" before Gazzer and Diesel ran up to the car and gave him a 'nark'.

We all ran, the look on his face resembling thunder. He simply left the car running and sprinted after all five of us down the road. We headed to the road works at the top of Cromson Street on the command of Diesel, who had taken it upon himself to lead this particular operation. "Get a cone each and put it on the corner of Clough Lane!" he shouted.

I was not sure what his plan was but we all did this with our new companion gaining ground. Then it clicked. Our friend turned the corner, trying obviously to catch us, and went head over heels as he hit the cones that we had lined up. We turned round very quickly and howled with laughter. He held his shin and shouted every insult under the sun. Hiding behind the wall of the textile factory, from where we could see the abandoned car, we waited for the driver to reclaim his vehicle. He hobbled to it, cursing and, I must admit, amidst the laughter, that I felt a bit sorry for the bloke who would certainly have a nasty bruise the next day.

When the third car wound down the window, we found a little beauty. She was blond, in her early twenties and a shape to die for which Murph nearly did, but more of that later. I was a little stunned myself when I saw her and Gazzer and Diesel got their 'nark' in well before I said anything.

"You're in for it little boys!" she threatened, looking for a coin, "when my boyfriend gets hold of you!" She glanced at the telephone box over the road as she fumbled in the glove compartment. Having concluded that she was very 'anti' the situation, Smithy and I legged it down the main road after Diesel and Gazzer. Murph, whom we have observed to be not as sharp as he could be, stayed behind to presumably chat her up. As he often reminded us, he was sixteen now and needed to find a girlfriend. I do not think this was quite the right time, but there you go.

The four of us hid behind the factory wall again, as the car was more or less in the same place as the one before with the 'hop along'. "He's giving her a coin to call her boyfriend! What a dip stick!" commented Smithy. The latter, on occasions, of course did not have room to talk himself but his view of this situation was a hundred per cent correct. Once the girl had finished her call, Murph was still talking to her outside the phone box!

"We've got to do something," I said to the others. "The boyfriend is going to kill him. "

"That's right," agreed Diesel.

We left our hiding place and approached Murph, grabbing him by his good arm and pulling him round the corner onto Cromson Street. The girl was taken aback and ran to her car. Looking from the hedge row at the corner, we watched a blue sports car pull up behind her and a bloke about six and a half foot, and just as wide, got out and went to his partner's car window. That was it, we all flew over the school field towards the Raz, where we stayed for half an hour.

On reflection, it was a funny 'nark' but, potentially, before our intervention, Murph had been looking at another twelve months with a hospital specialist. However, this time for both arms and possibly a leg thrown in for good measure.

The run up to the exams was highly amusing and I am convinced that the revision that I did was effective because I was so chilled on the Street. The hedge hopping which we did was comical, always getting a laugh, but on one evening, we had a brush with the law that was a little too close for comfort, although the lads never would have admitted it.

It was a Saturday night towards the end of June and the majority of the finals were out of the way, for those who had actually bothered to turn up. Murph did miss several, as mentioned previously, but Diesel and Gazzer also thought it unnecessary from time to time to put pen to paper in the examination hall! However, they did sit their maths and English, which they announced with a certain element of pride when their future lives in the marines cropped up in conversation. Apparently, the exams were a breeze, and they could work out the questions using logic and common sense without the need of reading through a book before they went in. I just hoped that the examiner marking their papers agreed.

A bottle of whiskey had been passed around the Wall, some drinking more than others, and this had fuelled a little Dutch courage.

"How about Springwater Avenue!" shouted Diesel, without any former reference to it. It's got loads of hedges and we've not done if for a while. "

It was a ten-minute walk to get there and subsequently we did not 'visit' much and when we did, we only hopped nine or ten hedges, not the whole street as Diesel then suggested. "Let's do the whole lot of them, lads," he continued, "from the top of the hill and all the way down to the bottom. Who's up for it?" We all nodded, Larry and Chad doing so with a little trepidation. We were entering the practically unknown and I'm sure that all of us felt a tinge of anxiety, Diesel included. However, as always, nothing was actually said which would point to a weak link in the crew and we all set off to Springwater, the whiskey bottle almost drained.

Once there, and almost with military precision, Gazzer plotted out the 'hop' and even had an escape route if things did not go to plan. "The garage at the bottom," he whispered, "has a flat roof and you can get onto the main street and leg it halfway to town, if need be. "He grinned, looking content with what he believed to be a failsafe plan. Murph was going to run along the pavement and 'marshall' the proceedings as he and a hedge had experienced, as we know, an altercation in the past.

"Alright, lads, let's go!" shouted Diesel, and the six of us jumped the first dividing garden hedge without too much problem, then the second and the third, amidst howls of laughter and yells of encouragement between us. This attracted attention and curtains began to twitch. The fourth house had its curtains open anyway and, Diesel being the joker that he was, stopped to do a funny wave to the occupants of the lounge followed by a 'nark'. This obviously caused the laughter to get louder and the spectators in Springwater to increase. By the time we arrived at the tenth hedge or thereabouts, the street looked like a Christmas tree, but the brief was to do the hop from top to bottom and that is what we continued to do. The challenge was so exhilarating that we were operating on adrenaline and I am sure that we could have done all twenty-three houses and escaped without incident but for Smithy falling near the end of the row of houses.

He had become winded and was struggling for breath. We quickly got hold of him and took him to one side in the shelter of some large bushes in one of the gardens. It was still light, and we did not make a sound. We were simply playing for time until Smithy was OK and then we would bolt.

People were coming out of their houses, looking behind walls and hedge rows and we were somewhat alarmed when one of them yelled, "That's more than enough for tonight. Call the police!"

"Coppers," whispered Chad anxiously.

"He's still wheezing, Chad," observed Larry.

"Come on," said Murph, who had joined us from the roadway. "Try to get your breath. "

Gazzer tapped Smithy on the back. He was slowly improving but the tick tock in my head gradually faded and was replaced by the sound of a siren. "We've got to move," murmured Diesel to Smithy. "Follow me and I'll give you a leg up over the garage. " Smithy nodded and we sprinted to it.

"Murph!" cried Gazzer. "Leg up at garage! "He elevated Murph onto the flat roof of the building whilst Diesel was doing the same for Smithy.

A police van stopped sharply on the pavement near some residents, wobbling as it did so. There were still five of us yet to scale the wall, but we did not waste any time in doing so as what only can be described as a stout copper, was talking to the group of people who were now in the middle of the road, pointing at us whilst we executed our escape. The copper started running down the street in our direction, which Murph and Smithy made crystal clear to us as they tried to help us onto the top of the building.

Everybody had made it except for Larry who was scrambling up the wall with the help from Chad and myself. His left leg dangled as we pulled him over the side, and the plump official swung out his arm in an attempt to grab his foot which he fortunately missed. Another police car had arrived by that time and a policeman more suitably built for the chase ran to assist his colleague who simply could not climb the wall. We watched briefly, as the entertainment value was immense. "You need to keep off the pies, 'Mr Plod'!" shouted Gazzer as he sped off with the rest of us. Murph and Smithy were quickly helped down from the roof and the rest of us hung from it dropping onto the front garden.

As we legged it down the street, we all took off our T shirts and tied them around our waists so as to look at least a little different to when the police last saw us. We ended up hiding in an empty skip that had been dumped outside a house in a side road. The smell was absolutely suffocating and debris on the side of the container rubbed off onto our skin.

"You'll need a bath before you see Suzy tomorrow, Chad," joked Gazzer as we lay in the skip.

"If I get out of this, I'll willingly have a bath to see her," he replied, laughing.

"I'm getting too old for this routine," piped up Larry. We all sniggered as quietly as we could.

"That copper," added Gazzer, "he was red in the face because he couldn't climb the wall. Why did they send him?" Laughter echoed in the skip as the sirens sounded outside of it.

However, these eventually disappeared, and we carefully headed to the Wall, taking the back streets. We talked briefly of the snap shots of the night-Diesels 'nark' at the lounge window, the residents searching for us under the hedge rows, the latter pointing at us from the middle of the road, the red face of the rotund caped crusader, his miserable efforts to scale the garage wall and his little friend running to help him.

We howled with laughter on our return, we really did, and to this very day, whenever we mention it in the pub, we end up breaking down into fits of laughter and the people around us, who do not know us, either laugh along with us, or walk away, carrying their drinks with worried looks on their faces.

CHAPTER 12

'The golf course'

A year earlier in June 1982, the US Golf Open was all over the television screens and being inspired by the professionals, we all took to the field opposite the Wall to practise our strokes. The patch where the bonfire had been the previous year had since grown over and our friends at the council had kindly cut the grass recently, so as to give us an even surface on which to play. How helpful they could be when they wanted to be.

I had my driver, my seven iron and my putter which I had bought second hand at the golf shop where I caddied at the weekend, and the others brought out a weird and wonderful array of golf clubs. Some brand spanking new and others with their handle grips balding and metal rusting at the edges. Needless to say, Chad had a sparkling set of Slazenger clubs just off the rack with a blue and red golf bag which Suzy held from time to time as her boy played his shots.

In stark contrast, Diesel carried around an old driver and putter that his grand dad had given him when he was alive. If he needed to chip a ball, he asked around for a seven or nine iron, hoping that one was available.

Gazzer was even less equipped, dragging around a rusty putter which he had dug out of his dad's attic. He used some clubs more than the owner himself. On one occasion, I lent him my seven iron and did not see it until the end of the day. Consequently, I was continuously borrowing irons from Chad and Larry.

The latter had a decent set of clubs and he was a good player. Displaying plenty of patience and immense concentration, he would drive the ball with a good length, setting himself up nicely for the put. He would do a little swagger of the hips in the process that would bring a smirk to some of our faces as we watched the ball fly down the field.

Smithy fancied himself as a bit of a golfer. He was not a bad player. He was average as we were, except Murph who could not play for toffee. However, he thought that he was better than Larry and would offer tips to him as he teed off or when he was putting the ball. Larry, being a quiet lad, would humour him as he watched on, but it aroused sniggers amongst the rest of us which more often than not were met by the two-finger salute from our golfing 'pro'.

As mentioned, Murph did not know which end of the golf club to hit the ball with and this brought about a most amusing incident on the field four or five days into the activity.

He was lining up to tee off, using Chad's driver, as he did not possess any golf clubs of his own. Then with a more confused look on his face than was customary, he swung the driver towards the ball. He did make contact with it which was an achievement for him because the majority of the time he simply missed it. However, it went in the wrong direction and went hurtling towards one of the garages on the edge of the field, hitting the side of it just below the window. The loud thud was followed by a shout which sounded familiar. It was of course our mate 'Johnny-know-it-all'.

"You nearly smashed Percy's window!" he yelled from the top of the hill. "What do you think you lot are doing?"

"It's Murph," I replied, "he's not too clever with the clubs, Mr Walton. "

"Not too clever with the clubs!" Johnny exclaimed, "this field is too small for golf!"

"He pulled on the dog's lead, telling it to sit down.

"Didn't you used to play golf when you were younger? "shouted Gazzer, trying to suppress his laughter.

"Listen sonny!" retorted our friend, "I too used to play golf when I was a lad and would probably do nine holes at the same time as you would take to do two or three but I practised on waste ground, away from residential areas. Not near them!"

A lecture, I felt was in the offing and I quickly piped up, "We're off to the woods now Mr Walton. We only came here to warm up. "

"If I hear any windows go, I know who to speak to," he responded and left pulling his dog behind him.

We concealed our laughter as best we could until Johnny was out of sight and then released it, rolling in the aisles.

"He is such a tool!" cried Diesel, putting both his clubs in one hand.

"I was ready to moony the bloke!" cried Murph. "Either that or send a golf ball through his window!"

"Your aim isn't good enough, Murph," said Gazzer, laughing. "It would probably end up in his chimney. "

All of the lads except Chad found the remark highly amusing.

"What's wrong Chad?" I inquired.

"Nothing," he replied. "I just don't fancy the idea of pulling my clubs to the woods. "

"No," I replied with a grin, "I just said that to shut Johnny up. What about if we all dump our stuff, meet up at the Wall and then have a walk over to the golf course and see what the golfers have to say?"

Everyone smirked as Smithy mentioned that he needed a few new golf balls to replace the ones he had lost on the field, so a visit would be useful. Not only useful but also a laugh, I thought.

We met half an hour or so later and made our way to the bottom of Clough Lane where the club was located.

We needed to cross the car park to gain access to the course and when we got there, a couple of golfers were taking bags out of a car boot and exchanging pleasantries. Hidden behind the concrete panels, we waited for the two blokes to end their banter so we could get on with our 'visit'.

"Come on," whispered Smithy, "we haven't got all day. That bald one is definitely going to get a ragging and he'll be a few balls lighter by the time he gets to the eighteenth. "

I gently waved my hand to quiet the laughter, grinning myself.

It was true that the golfer who was going a little thin on top was prolonging the conversation and in turn delaying us. Finally, however they finished their chat and disappeared through the official entrance on the other side of the car park, allowing us to scale the wall and drop down to the other side.

The sixth hole which was the nearest to where we were, was one of the better locations to bag a few balls. It would be a while before our bald friend and his mate appeared on the scene, so we lay in wait for other unsuspecting golfers near the green, ready to pocket their golf balls.

Chad had brought some binoculars as he did each year when we got up to this routine in the golfing season. He spotted a group of seven golfers making their way to the teeing off area for the hole, their bags bulging with golf balls. Diesel noted that they would need them as the first balls that they sent over would not be on the green for long.

Chad passed me the binoculars and the blokes laughed and joked as they teed off. The balls fell on the fairway and one by one they eventually arrived on the green. At this point, the golfers took a short cut to the green through a small wood, thus losing sight of the hole and more importantly of us.

"I'll get them," whispered Gazzer and quickly gathered the golf balls in an old supermarket bag. He returned back to cover walking backwards, his eyes fixed on the wood. A marine in the making for sure!

We then retreated further back where we hid behind some trees so that we could see the golfers' faces without them seeing ours! It was a process that we had done many times on this hole.

The reaction was priceless. We passed around the binoculars, creased up as we focussed the lenses on their expressions. Some looked irritated and others confused. One was even laughing to himself, a ball snatcher himself in the past, no doubt. A couple started to hack at some bushes with their clubs and three others walked back to the trees, looking behind them. The futility of their actions was hilarious and how they did not hear our laughter, I will never know. They eventually gave up the search for the 'lost' balls and teed off for the next hole.

This happened three times and the bags filled up with the booty. Of course, the players moved on, so they did not have chance to relay the tale to the ones that followed. Presumably they would exchange notes at the club house after the eighteenth but by that time we would be long gone.

Happy with our pickings, we waited for the bald man and his buddy from the car park, purely for entertainment reasons. We did not need any more golf balls. After a short while, we got a sighting. "Spotted them," murmured Chad, passing over the binoculars.

"Deep in conversation for a change," I noted as I sharpened the focus of the lenses.

"They won't be chatting away once we've finished with them," said Smithy, grinning as he reached for the 'bins'.

"Let them come out of the short cut," interjected Gazzer, "and then we'll coat them good and proper. "

Smiles appeared all around.

"Be careful Tod," muttered Larry, "you don't want them to recognise you when you're out caddying on a weekend. You'll lose your job. "

Larry was of course right. Once the exchange of words had taken place, I intended to be running before they really knew what was going on, just showing the back of my head which would be covered by my cap.

"You don't want to lose your job," added Murph, stating the obvious, surprisingly.

I swiftly turned my attention to the whereabouts of our two new friends. They were walking down the fairway at this point, preparing to chip the balls onto the green, still laughing and joking as they went. To be fair, they played decent shots when they got round to doing this, but we were not there to appreciate their strokes. When they walked out of the short cut, Diesel was the first to make his opinions known,

"Hey, baldy!" he yelled, "you've got a big nose and you can't play golf!"

I was already running before he finished his last sentence, giving a 'nark' as I went.

Not to single anybody out, Gazzer made an equally amusing comment about the other guy who, for the record, was very tall and slim. "Baldy!" he cried, "tell your mate not to walk over a course drain. He'll fall down the grid!"

The lads started to run at different times, and I believe that Smithy and Murph were the last to take to their heels after showing our follicly challenged buddy a brief moony.

The two blokes, after getting over the shock of what was happening, dropped everything and chased us down the fairway. We howled with laughter as we sprinted, and I think that Gazzer and Murph even found time to show them two fingers during the chase.

That said, the golfers were not hanging about and we needed to get off the course as soon as possible. We headed to the seventh hole where there was a bridge that we used to get into the woods, not far from the aerial runway and the slag heaps which you may remember.

However, the laughter soon dried up when we discovered that the bridge was not accessible because they were doing work on the timber. Barbed wire blocked the entrance. We had two irates on our heels and an escape route was urgently required. The car park would be full of golfers and the club house near the exit at the eighteenth would present the same problem.

"What are we going to do Tod?" shouted Murph as we did a U turn.

"Eighth hole!" I screamed, "over the nettle bushes and onto the main road. "

It must have looked comical as 'baldy' and his mate followed suit, doing a U turn as they continued the chase. I have never been so desperate to see a nettle bush, like ever. All seven of us scrambled over the nettles, our arms and hands stinging as we did so. However, powered by adrenaline, we only felt the full effects, once we were back at the Wall.

Smithy had been struggling with his breathing after the U turn and just about tumbled over the nettles with help from Larry and Gazzer before our golfing friends got there. Fortunately, they did not want to tackle the bushes. We heard, "We'll see you again, you little gets!" as we sped down the road. However, as long as they were no longer on our tail, we were not too concerned about their views on the matter.

We all eventually met up at the Wall, red, blotchy and suffering from the sting of the nettles. Chad handed out some dock leaves that he had collected on the way with a grin on his face. "Well lads," he asked, "was it worth it?"

We all laughed as we shared out the golf balls, nodding our heads. Of course, it had been worth it. The day had been a scream from start to finish.

CHAPTER 13

'Bike ride to Southport'

After the incident with Larry at the Raz in July '82, we decided that a further visit to the reservoir was not an option for a while and having time to fill, we took to our bikes.

We all had one, but they varied in appearance and performance! Chad had the fastest, you will not be surprised to hear, made of aluminium with five gears, whilst at the other end of the spectrum, Murph had an old rusting racer which did have three gears, admittedly, but only one of them worked. Mine was in between the two. A secondhand chopper with three gears, a little rusty in places, there was no denying. Nonetheless, I thought it was great and looked after it as best I could.

After doing a few local runs to town and back , we became more confident and ambitious in the saddle and it was not long before a trip to Southport was planned. It would take two and half hours to get there, but it was a nice location with sea, sand, funfair and as Diesel and Gazzer reminded us, plenty of girls who would be up for it.

The night before the ride, we met up at the Wall to discuss the routing and the plan for the day, but Smithy had something else on his mind.

"What about the munches," he said with a grin. "We'll need plenty of grub with all that riding. "

We all agreed but we had planned to take some sandwiches, which Chad explained to him, but Smithy had other ideas.

"We could always use some of Johnny's apples couldn't we," he added. "They're always nice and juicy. Ideal for a hot summer's day!"

Smirks appeared on everybody's faces and I could feel a plan on its way on how to plunder his apple tree which was bursting with life and tasty apples.

We knew that Johnny did like to have a snooze in the evening in front of the TV, but whether he would be asleep that night, was another story. His dog could also be an issue as it lay in front of the patio doors looking onto the garden.

"I'll be look out if you want," suggested Smithy, still grinning as he looked at Johnny's fence over the field.

"Yeah, nice one," replied Gazzer who as a future marine had already planned out the campaign. "Larry and Murph can give me, Diese, Chad and Tod a leg up over the fence and then wait for us to throw the bags of apples over. I'll then give the other three a leg up back and then climb the fence with a bit of help from you lot on the other side. "

In theory it was a good plan, but this was assuming that Johnny boy was asleep, and his faithful companion was away with the fairies. However, as always, there were no weak links in the chain, or none visible anyway, and the plan went into action.

Smithy was the first over the fence and was under the misconception, I sensed, that he was some kind of rugged mercenary, throwing caution to the wind in the pursuit of his goal. As we lifted him over the fence, he looked at us through his jam jar glasses with an air of determination and gave a thumbs up before jumping into the garden and scurrying behind a bush near Johnny's patio door. He remained silent which meant that both our buddy and the dog were snoozing and me and the other three were hurtled over the fence, each holding a crumpled carrier bag.

We feverishly filled the bags with the well-formed apples. "No noise," whispered Gazzer as he divided his attention between the tree and the back door. There were no more signs from Smithy, so everything seemed to be going to plan.

However, we had not accounted for the pressure that we had put on Johnny's fence when we first piled over it. It had been weakened in places and although Diesel, Smithy, Chad and I got away with our escape after taking the apples, the fence buckled under Gazzer's weight and the wood cracked, making a piercing sound that woke up the dog. Barking was followed by the switching on of a light and then Johnny boy running into his garden.

"What's going on!" he shouted, fumbling with the torch. He just caught the bottom of Gazzer's trainers with the beam as we pulled our partner in crime over the splintered wood. Blood poured from his right arm, soaking the timber panels, but pumped with adrenaline, I am not sure that he even felt it as we fled across the field. The plastic bags bulged with the apples as we sprinted to the safety of Darcy's tractor shed. Fortunately we did not see Johnny again that night!

The following day, it was a glorious Sunday morning and we all met at the Wall at eight o'clock on the dot in preparation for our journey to Southport. The apples that we shared out at Darcy's, the previous night, were stuffed into our back packs, together with bottles of water, crisps and heaven knows whatever else.

"A bit of a close shave last night, eh Gazzer?" commented Murph in his usual razor sharp fashion.

"You're not kidding," laughed Gazzer, showing everybody his bandaged arm, " but it won't stop me having a laugh today. It might even improve my chances with the chicks. The sympathy vote. "He winked at Diesel who smiled as he tested out the breaks on his racer.

"You got it in one, Gaz," responded his mate.

Just above the laughter, you could hear my shouts to get going, and we all set off, wearing shorts and T shirts to keep cool. Having the fastest bike, Chad led the pack as we got onto the first of our roads, namely the one going from Manchester to Liverpool. Smithy and Murph took the rear for different reasons. Smithy, as we have seen, was not the fittest member of the team, and Murph had just first gear available, so he only did the same work as the rest of us when we were going up a slope. On the flat, he was peddling twice as much.

It was hilarious when you turned around. All you could see was a pair of legs going ten to the dozen and a bright red face. Diesel nearly fell off the bike when he caught a glimpse of Murph, for laughing. A passing van sounded its horn because the bike was wobbling so much!

As we approached half way, we stopped for a break in one of the lay-bys of the road leading to Chorley. Murph was huffing and puffing as he got off his bike.

"You'll never be a marine Murph!" shouted Gazzer with a grin as he lay his bike on the ground.

"Don't want to be," replied Murph, taking off his small rucksack, the back of which was soaked in sweat.

"Alright Smithy?" asked Larry in a concerned tone as he saw him holding his side.

"Yeah," Smithy responded, "just picked up a stitch, that's all. "

"It's the only thing he will pick up today," muttered Diesel. "He won't be able to handle a bird in Southport. He'll be half dead at this rate. "

Gazzer and I were in earshot of the remark and our lips began to curl, developing into a suppressed snigger.

"Glad you find it funny lads!" shouted over Smithy, pulling out a bottle of water from his back pack and one of Johnny's apples.

"We weren't laughing at you mate," I responded, trying to keep the piece. "Gazzer was talking of how crap his bike was. "

He munched on the apple and watched the vehicles pass by, paying no attention to the comment. As we talked about the funfair, he started to take an interest in the conversation again however, adding ideas to those already offered of how we were going to get into the complex without paying. We had a bit of money on us but far from what we needed to pay the admission. Chad said that he was not paying if nobody else was, to which Larry agreed, and that he was pretty confident that a solution would be found once we were there.

Before setting off for the remainder of the journey, we all agreed to ride a little slower as Murph and Smithy had clearly struggled in the first half of the journey. The ride was still a laugh, especially when Chad nearly went into a tree due to an awkward red light forcing him to apply his breaks somewhat abruptly, but we wanted Murph and Smithy to reach the destination, rather than spend the night in a hospital somewhere on the way.

The more ground we covered, the more excited the lads became. Gazzer and Diesel shouted about the girls on the beach as they pedalled and Murph touched on the subject, saying that when he walked in the complex, the chicks, as he put it, would be swarming around him. His thoughts brought a smile to my face, turning quickly into a laugh. Firstly, it was very unlikely that this would happen, secondly, even if they did approach him, he was that worn out that he would be incapable of doing anything, and thirdly we had not even worked out how to get into the funfair for free. His opinions had the same effect on the others, possibly for the same reasons.

The smell of sea air got stronger and the sound of the sea gulls got louder, and it was not long before the frame of the roller coaster could be seen in the distance.

"We've made it!" yelled Chad who was still at the helm.

The cheers from the lads were deafening and Larry pointed out a sign showing the direction to the pier.

The sun was shining and the sky blue, making the girls on the beach look even more mouth watering in their bikinis. We dumped our bikes near the sea wall and ran down to the sand, trying to find a spot from where we could keep an eye on them. It would be a long walk home if they disappeared, that was for sure! Gazzer and Diesel also noted, quite rightly, that we also had to consider close proximity to decent looking girls. After taking all factors into consideration, we finally found a place and threw our rucksacks down, claiming the plot for a while.

Larry and Chad headed off to the sea almost immediately to cool down, and after getting an eyeful of the two 'stunners' near us, I joined them. As I came up for air whilst swimming under water, I noticed that Gazzer and Diesel had already approached the two beauties. They were doing press ups and sit ups on the sand, and from the look on the girls' faces, the lads' aim to impress was working.

"Didn't take them long," said Chad, smiling as he watched the boys in action on the walk back from the sea.

"It never does, Chad," I replied, laughing, "with or without a bandage on the arm. "

We also found it amusing, all three of us, when we saw Smithy and Murph trying their luck with a couple of girls further down the beach. They were doing salsa steps which were well executed, but the girls made it abundantly clear that there was no interest there when they rolled up their towels and showed two fingers to the lads, before finding somewhere else to lay down. "That is priceless!" I shouted to the other two who nodded their heads as they chuckled aloud.

"Tod!" cried Gazzer from his new plot as I was about to sit down and grab one of Johnny's apples out of my bag. "Yes, Gaz!" I replied.

"Tina's brother works on the gate of the fair. What does that say to you?"

It said a lot. All our prayers had been answered. Cinderella, you will go the ball, I thought. Chad and Larry who had obviously overheard the news had grins spreading from one side of their faces to the other, and when our defeated warriors returned back to camp, their mood swing was immense, on hearing what we had to tell them.

Not wasting any time, Tina and her friend Michelle packed up, and we slung our rucksacks on our backs, walking back to the bikes. Gazzer and Diesel went in the same direction. The former with his bandaged arm around Tina , and his mate doing the same with Michelle. The girls were wearing matching T shirts and shorts and they looked pretty tasty. The lads had done well in more ways than one!

There were bike stands all around the entrance to the funfair and we locked ours up before making our way to the gate where Tina's brother worked. She told us to wait while she went over to him and after a brief chat, she hugged him. In the process he passed something to her which you would have missed if you had not been looking for it.

On her return it became apparent what had happened. She dished out passes to all of us most discretely and suggested that we did not use the gate where her brother worked to enter the fair, so as to avoid suspicion.

Once in, we had a whale of a time, a real hoot. We did not see much of Gazzer, as you might expect, as he spent the majority of the time behind the Waltzer platform with Tina, and Diesel made himself scarce quite often also, finding similar locations with Michelle.

Smithy, Larry, Murph, Chad and I went on the roller coaster twice as it was so exhilarating, but on the second occasion, Murph, who had been munching on the apples between the two rides, was sick everywhere in the carriage. Revenge would have delighted Johnny boy, had he known about it, I am sure, but the fairground operatives were far from happy when we returned back to the boarding area!

On the dodgems, Smithy thought that he was a formula one racing driver for a while until Chad burst his bubble, sending his car flying across the floor, Smithy just managing to stay in his seat. Hilarious!

We met a few girls in the tea cups, one of whom took a liking to Chad, the latter quickly showing the interested party a picture of Suzy in his wallet. Chad later said that if Suzy had found out, she probably would have got the train to Southport and hunted her down. That would have been a distinct possibility!

We had such a scream that time flew by, and it was only when Larry looked at his watch that we realised that we would, at some point, have to go home.

Nobody could believe it was six o'clock, and what is more, no one was eager to do a two and a half hour journey back to Salford by bike. However, what choice did we have? We had no other options until the hero of the day turned up with Tina a little later, looking ever so content for a couple of reasons. The first was obvious. However the second cause for joy could be shared by all.

After another chat with her brother, Tina had persuaded him to give us all a lift back to the Wall in his van which was big enough for the whole crew and the bikes!

Elated, we waited an hour or so for the van to turn up. Gazzer and Diesel put the extra time to good use of course, and on the way home, amidst the clattering of bikes and the crunching of apples, we howled with laughter as we discussed the day.

When I asked Gaz how he managed to get the lift, he simply smiled and said that Tina wanted him to stay longer at the fair and offered her brother's services in return. When asked if he would see her again, he just put his thumbs up and said that if we were ever in Southport again, there was a fair chance.

CHAPTER 14

'The scout hut'

The six week holidays of '82 passed with break neck speed as they always do when you are having a hoot, and we were soon in August.

There had been an old hut belonging to the church on Cromson Street for many years, near the field. It was used for the odd Parish event and recently hired by a scout group to hold their meetings on a Thursday night. Needless to say we had 'visited' the 'troopers' on more than one occasion since the its opening, their reactions proving to be most hilarious. We would run up to the door and yell, "Dib, dib, dob, dib, dib, dob, you are such an ugly mob!" or "Akela, we will do our best!" putting great emphasis on the word 'will'. The comments on their own wound them up of course, but the fact that they referred to the cubs when they were scouts made them even more irate which increased the entertainment value.

Taking the bait, the blue and yellow scarved regiment would chase us, and one of them carried his 'dagger' in a sheath attached to his belt as if he had an assignment in the perilous jungle from where he might not return! We called him 'Rambo' because he really did think that he was a tough guy, bless him. Tall and thin in build, with ginger hair and a pocked face, 'Rambo' would shout out orders to his fellow troops in the pursuit of the enemy, and hiding behind the garages or wherever we found ourselves, a few 'narks' were given to aggravate the situation!

The first Thursday in August was especially amusing and led eventually to a 'cease fire' between the two camps for a short time at least.

It was around seven o'clock when we met at the Wall that night and the scout meeting was already underway.

"Do you want to give the tools in the hut a run around tonight?" asked Smithy, playing on his pocket computer game.

"Why not," responded Diesel, "you can wind them lot up a treat, especially Rambo. That bloke's a spanner."

As we laughed in agreement, Murph piped up, "I'm feeling a bit daring tonight, lads. What about a moony in the doorway with a special message to Rambo?"

"What message would that be?" I enquired .

Murph looked perplexed which was not uncommon, but even more so with this question. Seeing that no reply was forthcoming, I offered an option. "How about 'especially for you'," I suggested, grinning at the others.

"Priceless!" shouted Gazzer as he started to howl with laughter, just as everybody else did.

"OK," continued Gazzer, trying to compose himself, "what about this for a plan? I'll open the hut door and Smithy and Diesel will shout 'dib, dib, dob' in the corridor. Murph will then run into the corridor and moony Rambo at the hall entrance, shouting, 'Rambo, this one's for you!' You'll then leave the hut putting this piece of wood under the door to slow them down on the way out."

'Rambo's face would be a picture! We all made our way to the hut except Chad who was going to call on Suzy and meet us later. Gazzer had his hand on the handle. "Ready lads?" he smirked. We nodded our heads with anticipation. Given access to the hut , Smithy and Diesel dived in, shouting 'dib, dib, dob,' and with almost military precision they came out, giving Murph space to perform his moony which he executed superbly with a cry of, "Especially for you, this one Rambo! There we go!"

I think that he got a little confused and mixed our two suggestions together, but the result was hilarious.

The ginger haired legionnaire bounded down the hall followed by his fellow troopers as Murph straightened himself up and ran out of the mission door, jamming it with the piece of wood that Gazzer had found on the Street.

"Come on Murph!" shouted Larry, "catch up!", and the crew sprinted towards the garages.

It was not long before Murph was back in the fold and we scurried behind an old asbestos garage, laying in wait for the commando and his regiment.

"He's got his knife out of the sheath, "whispered Gazzer. "What an absolute tool. "

It was true. 'Rambo' ran onto the field, brandishing his 'dagger'. "Come on then, you moonshine wonder," he shouted, "let's be having you!"

"He'll never use it," muttered Diesel. "He probably doesn't even know how to use it, dipstick. "

"How about if we do the 'nark chime' eh?" said Smithy, trying desperately to control his laughter as the legionnaire tried to find us behind the bushes near Johnny's fence on the opposite side of the field. The bloke's miles out. He needs some help. "

"Good thinking," responded Gazzer, grinning with Smithy. "Let's split up and do it. "

The 'nark chime' comprised of a person shouting 'nark' from a location and then finding another place to shout, as the others made their contribution in turn from their own places. They then found a new place to hide. In this way, you had time to find another place while the person in pursuit was distracted by the others.

Rambo and his men at arms were all over the place as the 'nark' chimed.

We struggled to keep the momentum going because we were all busting a gut in the process. However, keep the momentum we did and we made 'gingernut' look like an amateur, waving a knife around like a headless chicken.

The noise from the 'narking' and 'Rambo's' pathetic attempt to hunt us down with his blade had obviously aroused curiosity within the neighbourhood, including that of the scout leader. Appearing from the side door of the mission that allowed access to the field, he saw 'Rambo' running around with the knife. "Stop it!" he bellowed in a horrified tone, his arms crossed and his face blood red with anger. "Put the knife back in it's sheath, Keith!" he growled, "and get inside. That also goes for the rest of you!"

'Captain Keith' was no longer the ginger haired commando, brandishing his weapon. He had been reduced to an ashamed little boy with ideas above his station, which more accurately described his character.

"And you lot out there!" continued the scout master, "I want to see you as well. Put an end to this ridiculous situation!" He paused for a moment, and getting no response, he resumed his announcement as we sniggered heavily, putting our hands over our mouths to suppress the sound. "I know who you are," he carried on, "I saw a few of your faces earlier at the door and I know where you meet, so if we don't talk tonight, we will in the future. So what is it to be?" inquired the leader.

"What do you reckon Tod?" said Diesel. "Do you think it'll be a laugh. We'll be able to see Rambo squeal. "

He had a point and after a brief discussion, we thought it would be better to get it out of the way now with the bonus of seeing 'Rambo' reduced to a cinder.

"I'll speak to him," said Larry, "if we are going. "

We all nodded. It was unusual for him to take the lead. He came out from behind the garage where we had quickly gathered after the 'nark chime' had been abruptly brought to a halt by our friend at the mission door.

He made himself visible to the scout master. "My name is Larry. It's Andy, isn't it. That's your name. We will talk to you but if there's any aggro, we're out. Are you OK with that Andy?"

The scout leader seemed surprised that Larry had taken the trouble to find out his name and although still angry, he responded in a calmer tone, "OK Larry. The side door is open. You and your friends can come up, if you wish. "

It seemed strange being in the hall, because now me and the lads had been invited whereas in the past we had always forced entry. Andy lined us up and began his lecture.

"Do you think it is acceptable to charge around the field outside with a knife, Keith?" he inquired.

'Rambo' shook his head, looking highly embarrassed which I personally found hilarious and had to divert my attention to a cracked floor board to stop an outburst of laughter. I thought of how much it would cost to mend it, who would do it and when it could be done. Anything to take my mind off his unease. The others also were battling with the temptation to laugh.

The scout leader then turned his attention to Murph. "And you my friend," he said, "is it normal behaviour to start showing your behind in a public gathering?" He waited for a response but Murph just stared at the scout master. I am not sure whether he simply did not have an answer to the question which was often the case or if he was afraid to speak at the risk of breaking into a guffaw of laughter. Sensing that we would be there until midnight unless someone intervened, I spoke on his behalf. "You have turned a blind eye," I said, "to the capers outside for the last few weeks. Nothing has been mentioned. "

"Yes," replied the leader, "but for the last few weeks, people have not been showing their behinds in a public place, nor have they been running around with knives. This is a different level, would you not agree?"

It was true that 'Commando Keith' had been wielding a potentially dangerous weapon but as a few of them said at the garages, he would not have done anything with it. He was just a spanner and that was it.

Larry took a more diplomatic approach. "Well, what do you suggest Andy?"

"The whole social fabric between the scouts and yourselves is in tatters and if left, someone's going to get hurt. Keith's knife will be confiscated, of course, but it can always be replaced with something else. "

I glanced at 'Rambo's' face, as did the others after this declaration and our brave little soldier was almost in tears. I wanted to laugh again but I frantically tried to concentrate on the split floor board as I did earlier, to distract myself.

Larry thankfully asked a question not involving the knife. "And how would you repair the social fabric, Andy?" he asked.

"By putting the energy of the two parties into a positive rather than a negative. Perhaps a football match, for example. " replied the scout leader.

The prospect of playing football against 'Rambo' and his 'battalion' did not appeal to me but after the lecture, Larry made a few points at the Wall while we were waiting for Chad and Suzy.

"I know he's a spanner, Andy," he said, "but he just doesn't want anybody to get injured. "

"They'll be no one getting stabbed now," laughed Gazzer, "our buddy Keith does not have a knife any more. Did you see his face when Andy Pandy said he was going to take it from him. How I kept a straight face, I'll never know. "

"It was hilarious," I agreed, "but what do you think about this talk of a football match?" I asked. "I don't fancy playing with them lot. They're a strange set of lads. Let them spend their time in the hut tying reef knots and half hitches, not on a football field with us. "

Everybody nodded, although Larry did so a little reluctantly.

"Well how about this," he suggested. "Let's leave off them for a couple of weeks while the dust settles and then we can start again if you want. "

"Yeah, a couple of weeks," repeated Smithy, "and then they'll get it again. Rambo's toothless now so it won't be as funny but we can still take the piss out of them!"

We all laughed, Larry included, who was happy with the temporary 'cease fire' agreement, I sensed.

It was not long before Chad the 'magician' and Suzy appeared from around the corner. "How was the hut job?" he shouted.

"Come and sit down Chad, and you too Suzy," replied Smithy, "you'll be in stitches. "

Chad creased up as we told him the story and Suzy listened with a smile.

There was a short 'cease fire' while the dust settled, as Larry put it. However, it was not long before insults were hurled from one side of the field to the other again, without the wielding of a knife of course.

Larry did get involved but avoided Andy. He had obviously bonded a little with the scout master during the escapade and wanted to avoid an awkward situation, I think. He never said this openly of course because 'street cred' was key at the Wall.

CHAPTER 15

'The swimming pool'

After an entertaining Christmas, the New Year of '83 was soon upon us. The snow had disappeared but it was still bitterly cold, our breath condensing as we spoke.

We were all at the Wall one chilly January evening except Larry who was busy getting hay for his horse at old Darcy's. We had done so much in '82 and the year had been hilarious for the most part. However the day at the Raz could have been a disaster but for the actions of Smithy and a few others, who of course saved Larry's life.

He was being hailed as the hero of the year, but this suddenly turned sour when he began to suggest that he and water were kindred spirits.

"I could swim," he commented, "at the age of three and the rest is history. "

Even Murph found this difficult to believe. "Really?" he said. "That seems a bit young to me, Smithy. "

"Give me anything, Murph," replied Smithy, "to do with water- a moat, a float or a boat, and I'll deal with it without breaking a sweat. "

"What about fishing rods?" asked Diesel with a grin. "I seem to remember that you nearly broke Larry's rod at Harp Street and snapped the line last year. "

As everybody laughed we were surrounded by a mist from our breath, highlighted by the street lamp.

"That was just a bit of bad luck," replied Smithy. "It was a big fish. It gave me the run around. You can't account for that. "

"He's such a fool at times," muttered Gazzer in the earshot of Diesel and Chad who sniggered openly and Smithy, not hearing Gazzer's synopsis, inquired "Something amusing, lads?"

"No nothing," replied Chad quickly. "Do you swim for the school, Smithy? I've never seen you at practice at the pool. "

The question had obvious undertones of irony which I think Smithy would have picked up on but he did not let on.

"No Chad," he answered. "These days, I haven't got much time with the Wall and my computer and all that. But as I say in the water, I come into my own, and I don't think many would get near me, and that includes the Street. "

Whether he realised it or not, Smithy had thrown down the gauntlet and there was a mixture of smirks and looks of amazement on the faces of the lads and Suzy. The latter could not hold herself. She smoked on her cigarette, inhaling deeper than usual. "OK, Smithy," she said, "you seem pretty confident about your strokes. Why don't you race Chad at the pool in town and then we'll see if you are the best swimmer around. "

Chad looked at his girlfriend with a grin and covered his face with his hand for a second, wondering what Suzy had got him involved in. The rest of the lads laughed.

"So when's the date?" asked Gazzer, spluttering out his words for laughing.

Smithy's bold look had changed into one of fear, and the contrast added to the amusement.

"So when do you want to swim?" asked Chad, deciding to play along after having got over the shock, instigated by his ever so proud girlfriend.

Smithy knew that Chad swam for the school and I think at this point he realised that the comment that he had made earlier was somewhat naive. Some would say delusional. Nonetheless he did not want to lose face, anymore than he had, and replied, trying desperately to give an air of confidence, which was by no way convincing, I felt, "Next Wednesday night Chad. We'll see then. "

He scooted off, claiming that his supper would be overcooked if he left it any longer. However it was clear to us that he was quite literally out of his depth and a quick exit was the only option at that given time.

Wednesday soon arrived and the eight of us including Suzy met at the Wall around six o'clock. The two competitors were on opposite sides of the spectrum. So humorous. One was calm and collected holding his towel bag confidently, and the other had a worried look on his face which he was trying hopelessly to disguise. The atmosphere buzzed with excitement.

"Ready to go," grinned Diesel. We all nodded also with a grin except Smithy who obviously had things on his mind.

It was only a half an hour to the pool and Smithy was unusually quiet during the walk. Chad walked hand in hand with Suzy who looked behind at Smithy every now and again and smiled to herself.

We had a pass from school which got us into the building free of charge, twice a month, as our friends at the council wanted to encourage swimming within Salford schools. Most of us did not have the money for a ticket anyway, so it was a good job. When its a turnstile, passing without payment is much more difficult to do. Almost impossible in fact!

Of course, in the changing room, we all had a towel fight before going poolside, and again Smithy was not his normal self, not taking much interest in it.

We had a warm up before the main event and needless to say Diesel and Gazzer were out to impress a couple of girls that they had spotted almost immediately when they got to the pool. Just as the peacock opens it's patterned plumage to attract it's mate, the two lads performed countless dive bombs and the odd somersault. The girls clapped and cheered, and when Diesel sat on the side of the pool, feigning an injury to his foot due to a dive bomb that he purposely did incorrectly, one of the girls knelt at the side of him, showing concern. This developed into caressing between the two of them and then finally a 'snogging' session against the ladders in the corner of the deep end, alongside Gazzer and the other girl. They were brought together when discussing the 'problems' that Diesel had experienced during his dive bomb.

Dive bombing, somersaulting and petting were three activities amongst others that were not permitted in the pool and appeared on a large sign just as you entered it. Gazzer, Diesel and the two girls were not overly concerned about the detail in the request and neither was the life guard who was spending his time chatting up one of the ladies. I think that the official reason for the conversation was how to execute the butterfly stroke but I sensed that he had another agenda . However weighing up the attributes of the woman, I could not really blame him!

Murph did try his luck with the girl that Gazzer eventually ended up with. He went over to her, while she was talking to Gazzer about Diesel's exploits, trying to make her laugh with jokes that fell flat on their face, according to Gazzer. If there was any doubt where her interests lay, she made it crystal clear when she asked Gazzer if he had any training in mouth to mouth resuscitation, and if so to give it a go in the deep end with her. Murph later blamed his arm for the lack of success with Gazzer's eventual partner for the day because he could not perform as well as the others in the water. There was possibly more to it than that.

While the three lads had been occupied with the fairer sex, Chad had been preparing for the race under the watchful eye of his ever loving girlfriend Suzy who was shouting words of encouragement from the spectator section of the natatorium. I managed to speak to him on only one occasion as Suzy, being so driven as she was, asked me not to distract him while he was getting ready for the race. He told me that he was not going to leave Smithy standing because he had such a high regard for himself, that to do so would totally deflate him. A win of about a third of a length, he added, would put the record straight.

Smithy was obviously limbering up for the race in the pool and Larry, who was not a bad swimmer, was trying to give him a little last minute coaching. This carried on for twenty minutes or so, when I noticed a 'stunner' with red hair and a perfect figure approach Larry and start talking to him. She tried every trick in the book to get his attention but for some reason, he was more concerned about Smithy's swimming than with her. In fact, when she put her arm around him in a playful manner, he demonstrated a stroke used in the Crawl so that she was forced to move it away. Smithy, realising that Larry was not taking her on, tried to chat her up himself, but the interaction was short lived and she made her way to the changing rooms with a friend, looking rather upset. I would not have turned her down, that is for sure!

We all had yellow wrist bands which was the last group of the evening before the pool closed at nine o'clock. Seeing that it was approaching eight thirty, I pointed out the time to Chad and Smithy who, with a nod of the head, took their positions on the poolside. Chad looked calm as if it was just another day at the office whereas Smithy was apprehensive to say the least. I was wondering whether he would be able to function properly once he hit the water.

Larry, Murph and Suzy watched intensely as I counted down, just as Gazzer and Diesel did from the other side of the deep end with their companions. At the shout of zero, Smithy and Chad dived into the water and the contest was under way!

The task comprised of swimming five lengths using whichever stroke they wanted. Opting for the Crawl, Chad tore through the water as Suzy cheered like a screaming banshee, and his competitor, also choosing the same stroke, did his best to keep up. It soon became clear, however, that he was no match for Chad who slowed down, as he said he would do, after the third length, so as to give Smithy more of a chance. Slowing the pace, however, did not make any difference. As a matter of fact, Smithy was losing ground, if anything.

Chad later said that if he had reduced his speed any further, he would have sunk. He won the race by a length and a quarter. After completing his fifth length, Smithy climbed up the ladder to the poolside looking worn out and gasping for air. He had been literally blown out of the water into little pieces and, at one point, as he walked to the changing rooms, I thought that he was going to collapse. Gazzer even said that he felt sorry for the bloke and so did I to a certain degree.

After a final 'snog' with their newly found friends, Diesel and Gazzer joined us all in the changing room, where the atmosphere was strange. Smithy was disappointed by the outcome of the race to such a degree that Chad started to feel guilty about the whole thing.

However, Diesel summed it up well on the way home when he said to both Chad and Suzy that Smithy should not have come up with such a stupid comment at the Wall, suggesting that he was God's gift to swimming.

Would he learn from this, however, I asked myself. I was not sure that he would.

CHAPTER 16

'Skateboarding'

We were the Crommy Boys and the Black Wall was our second home. Some would say our first! However, there were other lads living on the Street or near to it who rarely made an appearance, and we often wondered what they did with their time. Maybe doing their homework all night, TV perhaps, walking the dog. It was beyond me and even thinking of it made me yawn. Life without the Street would send me mad.

One such lad was Hutchy, who lived just off Cromson Street. He had a short encounter with us in the summer of '82 when skateboarding was all the rage.

It was mid-August and the lads had their skateboards out that weekend from morning till night. Some of us had decent 'trucks' and others not so good. Chad had the Rolls Royce of skateboards which could do anything, even drive itself round a corner! Mine on the other hand, rather like Gazzer's and Diesel's, had rubbers on the wheels which were so hard that you just carried on in a straight line when you put pressure on them to turn. You were fortunate not to end up wrapped around a lamp post. Larry's and Smithy's skateboards were middle of the road and could turn without too much effort and Murph used his brother's skateboard which was quite good.

As we touched on earlier, the crew saw Hutchy only now and again when he was going to school or to the off licence for his mum, for example, so when he appeared on the Saturday morning, bright and breezy with his skateboard, it was quite a surprise.

"Hi there Hutchy," I said, tightening up the wheels of my board at the Wall. "We don't see you much round here. "

"No," he replied, "my mum always finds me things to do in the house and she's pretty keen with homework. "

Poor kid, I thought as I put down the spanner. Gazzer and Diesel had smirks developing on their faces and before these turned into outbursts of laughter, I asked, "Where did you get the skateboard. Top of the range, eh?"

Hutchy nodded proudly and responded, "My mum got if for me last month as a reward for passing my summer exams. "

"Exams, what are they?" cried Murph with a chuckle.

Hutchy made no reaction to Murph's remark and put his foot on the tail of his skateboard, amidst laughter from the rest of us.

I think that Gazzer and Diesel were laughing more at what had been said previously than at Murph's comment.

Chad inspected Hutchy's skateboard admiringly. "How fast can it go?" he asked. "You must be able to get some speed out of that. "

"Yeah, it can move," responded Hutchy. "Nine miles per hour on the flat and up to fourteen down-hill, with the wind. "

"That sounds like a challenge to me!" exclaimed Smithy, eyeing up Chad's skateboard on the pavement. "Can you go that fast, Chad?" he continued.

It did not seem like a challenge to me, more of an answer to a question, but the remark did provoke a suggestion from Diesel. "You've both got good trucks

Chad, why don't you see whose board is the fastest and can perform the best?" he said.

"I did not want to blow my own trumpet," responded Hutchy quickly, "but if Chad wants a contest for fun, we can do that. "

Chad smiled, picking up his skateboard. "Yeah, OK, you're on," he said. "We can use the traffic cones on Clough Lane to make a slalom and involve some skills. It's not all about speed. "

Smithy beamed with contentment. He had neither the skills or the 'truck' to be a serious contender in such a competition, but at least he was part of it because of his comments which had brought it about.

"So when do you want to do it?" inquired Chad, doing a kick flip on his board.

"How about if we practice until tea time and do it then," replied Hutchy, who was clearly enjoying the camaraderie amongst the lads.

Murph and Smithy went down Clough Lane to get the traffic cones for the slalom, while Chad and Hutchy were practising. Apparently, according to Smithy, he walked back with four of them on his head, shouting that he was a good wizard who could cure people of their ills. First of all, he was not a wizard and secondly, he was making it public that we were 'borrowing' cones from the council which was of course illegal. Spanner!

It was agreed between Chad and Hutchy that besides doing the slalom, they would also do a kick flip, a heel flip, an axle stall and a board slide, which were constantly being demonstrated by the two of them, in between doing the slalom, consisting of four traffic cones.

The others, including myself were also on our 'trucks', but Diesel, Gazzer and myself were continually knocking over the cones because we could not direct the boards, due to the rubbers being like blocks of stone. In fact, Gazzer went into a cone and fell off, bruising the same arm that he cut on Johnny's fence three or four weeks previously, during the apple raid.

Larry managed to perform one or two tricks, but Smithy and Murph did make a few of us smile when they tried to copy Chad and Hutchy. They only did half a trick because of their limitations, but made out that they had executed it fully with the odd comment of self praise and a look of great accomplishment. Diesel said that they were dipsticks and I could not argue.

The day galloped on by and before we knew it, the time for the race had come. The competitors made their way to the starting line and waited side by side for the count down. They were required to do the four tricks, then the slalom, and finish with a sprint down the hill to the line near the school gates at the bottom of Cromson Street.

Chad looked calm as Chad usually did and Hutchy had a look of determination about him and looked in good shape.

"Three, two, one!" I yelled and the two of them set off. The wheels of the 'trucks' rattled as they did the kick and heel flip and the wood of the board grated against the kerb, whilst they performed the board slide. They were in tandem during the display of tricks and it looked rather impressive. After the axle stall, they negotiated the cones, resembling a soldier, zigzagging to avoid the volley of shots behind him.

At this point, they were neck and neck. I noticed Smithy's mild look of envy as he was probably picturing himself doing the same thing. Murph was trying to copy a couple of tricks but he did not quite get there.

On the final part of the course, they propelled themselves forward and the 'trucks' charged down the hill at speed, heading for the finish line.

Larry was at the line to adjudicate and Hutchy crossed it with only three or four inches to spare.

The race was spectacular and we all congratulated Hutchy on his win and also praised Chad for his performance.

Gazzer was one of the first to compliment the new addition to the crew, albeit on a temporary basis as it proved to be, and now he had respect for Hutchy rather than seeing him as a laughing stock.

"You won it fair and square, Hutch," said Chad, getting his breath back.

Hutchy just did a high five and said that he would see us the next day on the 'trucks'.

Unbeknown to us, the contest had aroused the curiosity of an unsavoury individual who lived on Clough Lane. He was called 'Lenny the loon' and was a loner who had been in and out of borstal since he was fifteen. He was now seventeen and lived with his alcoholic father. It later emerged that he became aware of the event because of Murph's clowning around with the cones on the Lane.

We all returned home that night quite innocently, not knowing what lay in store for us the next day.

We gathered at the Wall the following day, still chatting about the events of Saturday evening. Everybody was there except for Hutchy who had not yet surfaced.

"Hutchy might be a bit of a mummy's boy," remarked Diesel, "but he can certainly ride a truck, that's for sure. "

"Yeah, but he's got the best board around," piped up Smithy a little sourly as he moved to sit on his skateboard.

"He might have the best skateboard, Smithy," said Gazzer, "but you still have to know how to use it. "

Chad grinned, adding, "There's no doubt there and he can. "

As we talked about the four tricks that the lads did, Hutchy appeared from around the corner with a look of joy on his face, carrying the 'truck' at his side. "Alright guys," he said, "fancy a bit of boarding to get the morning underway?"

The lad was dedicated and he did twists and turns on the board, as we all did, but not as well, with the exception of Chad, of course.

However, there was a problem on the horizon and around dinner time or lunch time if you prefer to call it that, we saw 'Lenny the loon' cross Clough Lane and make his way towards us. He was heavily tattooed with cropped black hair and a scar across his cheek. We hardly ever saw him because he was either in the pub sat in a corner or 'inside', so it was bit of a shock when he approached us.

"Well, well, well," said Lenny in a menacing tone, "I see that the cones you took from the road works have not been returned yet. "

He looked at Murph with a threatening stare. "Does the wizard also return traffic cones besides curing people of their illnesses?" he asked, moving a little nearer to him.

To say that Murph was intimidated, was putting it mildly. If the launderette in town had been open on a Sunday morning, he would have been making his way to it.

"Sorry Len," he stammered. "Me and a few of the others are going to take them back after dinner. "

"Really?" responded Lenny, "Is that right?"

He turned his attention, then, to Hutchy. "Nice skateboard," he said with a grin. "I come from a poor family and I've learnt with time that if you cannot afford something that you want, you either rob the money to pay for it or take the thing itself. "

Hutchy was buckling, a mild panic settling in.

"How much is it worth?" asked Lenny, touching one of the rear wheels, "twenty, thirty, forty quid?"

Although flustered, Hutchy still managed to think on his feet, answering, "You guess. I'll show you what it can do. "

Lenny looked a little confused as Hutchy tilted the front of the skateboard upwards with a grin. However this soon turned into a combination of surprise and anger when the lad thrusted the board forward using the grip of his trainer, and hurtled down the hill. He was doing twelve or thirteen miles per hour, relentless in his aim to save the 'truck'. Larry was also determined, however, to get the board and sprinted after Hutchy with some speed, but not enough to catch his prey who propelled himself out of Cromson Street and sped to town. It later transpired that Lenny chased him almost all the way to town, but eventually gave up because he could not run any further.

Needless to say, we all got a lecture from Hutchy's mum the next day, who made it her business to have a 'chat' with us after finishing work. "Who is Tod?" she asked looking at our expressions for clues.

"That would be me, Mrs Hutchinson," I replied, getting to my feet.

"My son," she continued, "never leaves the house at night, and the moment he does, he gets chased by a brute who wants to steal his new skateboard. This shows how much society has decayed in our present day. It's like taking toffee from a small child. My poor Edward. "

"I can understand your feelings, Mrs Hutchinson," I replied, "but we are not to blame for what happened to your son. "

"I beg to differ," responded Hutchy's mum. "I believe that this scumbag's interest was aroused by an idiot amongst you who was shouting and bawling whilst collecting the traffic cones for the slalom, which, by the way is illegal. Now, I don't expect you'll tell me who the culprit is, not even my son will say, but I want to know where that ruffian lives, so that I can have a word with him. "

We all knew that if we gave that information, there was a distinct possibility that several of us, if not all, would end up with broken limbs. Something we wanted to avoid, of course.

"I don't know his address, Mrs Hutchinson," I responded, "and neither do the mates. I think he lives somewhere in town. "

"OK," she shouted furiously, "play it your way, but I will find him and, in the meantime, Edward, never goes out again. That's it!" and off she stormed to her front door.

Murph had been a complete tool with the traffic cones but we could obviously not inform on him because he was a member of the crew. However, he got an 'ear bashing' from the rest of us after Hutchy's mum left and as she said, we never saw him again on the Street.

118

CHAPTER 17

'The road show'

The trip to Southport had given us an appetite for the quest of new scenery and new faces, for a little time anyway, and when we heard about the Manchester Radio Road Show on Perry Lane in Salford, we were keen to go. It was nearly the end of a warm July in '82', the weather being ideal for the event.

Diesel's dad had agreed to take us to the show in his van which I am not sure was strictly legal, as it only had seats in the front for him and his son. He threw the rest of us, Smithy, Larry, Murph, Chad, Gazzer and me, into the back. As you may imagine, it was every man for himself to find somewhere to sit on the floor! He grinned as he marshalled us in, saying that we were young and it would not do us any harm. The majority of us had no bus fare anyway, so we really did not have a choice.

Our theme for the day at the road show was break dance, and wearing track suits and trainers, we limbered up in the van as best we could in the limited space available.

"Let's hope that there are some more decent chicks today lads, like there were at Southport!" shouted Diesel from the front. "That Michelle was fit!"

His dad smiled proudly adding, "Time to lock up your daughters when our Tez is in town!"

Laughter echoed in the back of the van, drowning out the noise from the old engine and the aging suspension.

"Once they see my jack hammer and caterpillar, they'll be flocking around us!" cried Gazzer, who had now lost the bandage after the escapades at Johnny's fence.

"Yeah," interjected Murph, "my salsa step is always a favourite with the girls. They can't get enough of it!"

As we howled with laughter, I was not sure whether we were laughing with Murph or at him, as his track record with the fairer sex was not at all impressive, it had be said. However he did at least try and that was something, I suppose.

"How about you Larry," said Smithy, "are you out to impress? I'm sure there'll be plenty of free girls out there today. "

I glanced at Larry for a response but he said nothing, just smiling uncomfortably as he continued with his warm up.

The squeaky brakes eventually brought the van to a halt on Perry Lane and we all piled out. As we thanked Diesel's dad for the lift, we could hear music blaring on Perry Fields, and the voice of the disc jockey, Sheeny, who was talking to the crowd.

"It's Sheeny, Chad!" cried Murph. "Do you remember, we listened to him a few weeks ago on your radio!"

Chad nodded as he straightened his cap. "That's right, Murph," he replied, "and this time we'll see him face to face. "

As we strolled to the gate, excitement and anticipation buzzed around us. Fortunately, there was no entrance fee and we found a spot amongst the hundreds of people there, not a million miles from the stage.

It was not long before Sheeny played the East Avenue Mob and without further ado, we started our routine on the old, crumbling piece of cardboard that we had brought.

Our show was defiant, bold, confident, rebellious and colourful, and soon caught the attention of the people around us. Gazzer did a combination of jack hammer, salsa step, caterpillar and head spin, whilst the rest of us did the salsa and Indian steps around him.

As nearby spectators started to cheer, we heard Sheeny yell on the microphone, "Break dance mania! Give the lads a cheer everybody!"

The noise became deafening as the whole crowd, it seemed, shouted and whistled in approval, and once East Avenue had sung their final line, there was a rapture of applause as we stood in a circle, beaming with contentment, pride and utter joy. An image of Petra's face suddenly appeared to me at the social club a few months earlier when she was watching me do the same thing. If only she was here now.

Sheeny interrupted my thoughts. "We'll speak later lads!" he cried. "I'll need one of you for a competition on stage later!"

The invite from the DJ did our 'street cred' a world of good and we were soon surrounded by, what only can be described, as excited females. Some were nothing to write home about, clearly , but there were several of whom you would write home about and we indulged ourselves in conversation with them.

Obviously, Diesel and Gazzer were in their element and quickly had their arms around two 'stunners', whilst Murph was trying his utmost to make hay while the sun shinned. He was doing fairly well with a nice looking girl until he did a salsa step which was intended to impress, but sent her flying instead when he caught her with his leg. Looking shocked as she got up, she walked off without a word, never to be seen again!

As we enjoyed our new found popularity, one of Sheeny's 'runners' made his way to me, Smithy and Murph who were the only ones there at the time. Gazzer and Diesel were busy behind the back of the ice cream van with their recent conquests and Larry and Chad had nipped off for a burger.

"Sheeny's doing a competition later," commented the 'runner', "to spot the biggest bore here. He's going to ask five really unexciting questions and the one who gets the most correct will be crowned 'Road Show Bore 1982'. Any offers?"

Murph was still getting over the salsa step incident and I certainly did not want to dint my 'street cred' with such a 'glamourous' title. However, Smithy thought differently. "I'm up for it," he replied. "The birds will love a road show bore. It's a right laugh. When do I go up?"

The 'runner' said that he would call him in about twenty minutes. I was not sure whether the girls would love a road show bore or feel sorry for such an individual. I suspected the latter, but we would see.

Word got around about Smithy's appearance and all the lads regrouped, together with our new guests. One was called Elsa who was hand in hand with Gazzer and the other girl was Agnes who was getting a 'piggy back' off Diesel. They were Swedish and were on the final day of a short visit to the north of England, with tickets to fly back to Stockholm later in the evening.

The 'runner' had collected Smithy and he was waiting with the four other guys to do the competition. Sheeny played out the last record and the 'runner' signalled to the five lads to go up the stairs.

"OK, folks!" announced the DJ, "Road Show Bore 1982! Give the contestants a cheer!"

The crowd cheered in anticipation as the participants took their seats at the side of the stage.

"Today, we are going to find out," continued Sheeny, "who amongst these five would send us to sleep on a night out for the greatest amount of time!"

The spectators screamed with laughter, waiting for the first player to get up. Sheeny quickly looked at the lads and pointed to Smithy to take his place on the podium. "And your name is?" inquired the DJ.

"Smithy," he answered.

"Smithy. That's an original name, isn't it? I'm starting to get sleepy already!" chuckled the host, feigning a yawn.

The audience loved the comment, howling with laughter, just as we did.

"They're going to crucify him!" cried Gazzer, nearly choking as he spoke. His partner of the moment, Elsa, was also in fits of laughter, and threw her head on his shoulder, her long blond hair tumbling down as she did so.

Smithy laughed along with Sheeny, still believing that his involvement in the quiz would enhance his profile and in turn bag him a beauty. However, I was curious to see if this would continue.

"Right, Mr Interesting," said Sheeny with a grin, "give me the value of pye up to five decimal places. "

From the response of the crowd, I do not think that half of them even knew what pye was. Many looked confused.

"3. 14159," answered Smithy with a smile, giving the DJ a pat on the shoulder.

The compare consulted his clip board and turned to the audience with a yawning gesture. "That's correct but where is my sleeping bag?" he yelled. "I'll need it with this one!"

The spectators roared with laughter, and at this stage I felt that Smithy was starting to realise that he had made a bad decision. He tried to hide his unease, of course, with a grin and a wave to the crowd, but I certainly could see through it and so could the rest of the lads.

"The bloke's a tool!" shouted Diesel. "They're taking the piss out of him!" Rather like Gazzer, Diesel also had a problem with his breathing because he was laughing so much and Agnes, his girl for the day, was splitting her sides.

Was Smithy delusional or naive? Probably a bit of both. I was busting a gut myself, but I could not help feeling a little sorry for the guy. The wannabe joker was now the joke.

As the merriment subsided a touch, Sheeny proceeded with his second question. "OK, Mr Maths!" he yelled with a snigger, "what is an isosceles triangle?" Whilst Smithy thought for a second, the host asked the audience to put up their hands if they knew and very few did.

"It's a triangle with two equal sides," he answered with a forced smile.

"With two equal sides," repeated Sheeny, glancing at his notes. "You're right mate, but whoever makes sleeping tablets should be on their guard because you would put them out of business!"

The spectators collapsed again with laughter, myself included. Why did he not just give a stupid answer? That would at least help to get the crowd on his side.

"Question three!" cried the DJ, wrestling to get his words out for chuckling. "What is Boyle's Law?"

"OK Sheeny," answered Smithy with a grin which was by no way genuine, "I think you'll find it says that the pressure of a given mass is inversely proportional to its volume. "

After checking the answer, the host screamed, "Right again, but you'll have to get me a cup of coco because after listening to that I'm ready for bed. Look at me, I'm half asleep, stood up, like a horse!" He looked at the crowd who were in stitches.

"Why doesn't he come down, Tod?" asked Chad.

"The damage has already been done, Chad," I answered. "He wanted the girls to love him. After this, they'll just feel sorry for the lad. "

"He won't get a bird after this!" cried Murph. It was an hypothesis that the rest of us would have struggled to arrive at.

As question four rolled out of Sheeny's lips, a few in the crowd, although still highly amused by the contest, were starting to feel a bit sorry for the boy with the jam jar glasses. I heard one or two comments around us, especially from the girls, like 'poor lad' and 'it's a shame'.

"What is the code," asked the compere, "of nitrogen dioxide?"

The audience waited with baited breath, their attention focussed on the stage. From the expression on his face, I think that Smithy was in two minds whether to answer correctly or not. After a short hiatus, he decided to go for accuracy, possibly realising that the point of return to rekindle any 'street cred' that he had was long gone.

"NO_2," he answered, a little defiantly.

Of course, the DJ burst into laughter, adding "OK, we'll give you that, but at this rate mate, you going to have me in a coma. I'm passed the sleeping stage now!"

Laughter bounced off the podium. All six of us and the two girls were on the verge of falling over because we were roaring that much with laughter.

Smithy was obviously well aware at this juncture of the proceedings that he was the joke and not the joker, and he signalled to Sheeny to bring over the microphone, which the DJ did quite willingly as he tried to control his laughter.

"What's the last one, Sheeny?" he asked with more defiance than before. "I'm after a full house. Five out of five."

The host chuckled loudly and replied, "The other four lads haven't got a chance with you around Smithy. You'd even send a bullfrog to sleep in the height of summer!"

Sheeny tried to shout over the crowd who were in fits of laughter. "Alright!" he yelled, "this is the final question. Tell me, what is an arthropod?"

"An invertebrate animal such as a spider," Smithy answered quickly with a smile.

"That's right!" cried the DJ, glancing at the audience. "I'm officially now in a coma. Call me an ambulance. I cannot take any more!" he continued with a chortle.

He indicated to Smithy to retake his seat while the crowd howled with laughter. Even Larry was going red in the face because he had been laughing so much. Smithy sat down brimming with defiance.

As touched on earlier, Smithy could be his worst own enemy. The experienced fisherman, the determined mercenary, the elite swimmer, the gifted golfer and now God's gift to comedy. The chasm between reality and his imaginary world could be immense, and although it was amusing for us, it was not such a hoot for him on the receiving end, surely.

After Smithy's grilling on the stage, the other four guys were not as forthcoming with correct answers as he was. The next two participants got all five questions wrong on purpose, I suspect, so as to laugh with the crowd rather than be mocked by them. The third answered his first question correctly, but sensing an onslaught from Sheeny and his buddies, he buckled and gave four absurd but amusing answers which won the audience back. The last guy battled to question three, giving correct responses, but could not take the heat any longer from the crowd, and deliberately got his two final questions wrong.

Smithy had been taken to the cleaners and back, and Sheeny had no trouble in deciding who the winner was of 'Road Show Boar 1982'.

"OK, folks!" he yelled, "one of the lads nearly sent me to sleep but Smithy had me unconscious because the time with him was so uninteresting. " There was a big emphasis on the last word, and the spectators screamed with laughter as Sheeny pinned a rosette on Smithy's T shirt, displaying the message, 'Road Show Bore 1982'. "Wear it with pride, mate!" shouted Sheeny as Smithy went down the stairs, "you deserve it, that much is for sure!" The DJ chortled, making his way to his sound system to play the next record.

"Well bud, he tore you apart up there," shouted Diesel to Smithy who was walking towards us, not looking so much defiant now but more deflated.

If there was any doubt about Smithy's chances with the girls for the rest of the event, Murph cleared them up. "Your street cred has gone, Smit," he exclaimed, "no girlies for you tonight. "

The remark aroused smirks on all our faces, although, looking back, this was a little heartless, facing the victim head on. Barely audible amongst the buzzing audience, he muttered, "I thought it would be good for the image because it was a laugh and I was on stage and all that, but they made me look like a geek. " Welcome to the real world, I thought, but I made no comments

As predicted, any female attention towards Smithy was a show of sympathy, and needless to say 'rough and tumble' was off the agenda. Gazzer and Diesel, on the other hand, were tied up with Elsa and Agnes for the rest of the evening behind the ice cream van, and as I said to Chad, I do not think that they were eating 'ninety nines'! Murph tried his luck with a few other girls as night approached but word had probably got around about his salsa step, and it did not come to much. Larry just listened to Sheeny's selection of tunes and chatted with the rest of us.

As darkness began to fall, Diesel and Gazzer returned with Agnes and Elsa, their faces glowing with contentment.

"We can get one more in the back," said Diesel with a grin. "After dropping us off, the girls have to take the hire car back to the airport and then get the plane to Stockholm. "

With all the hilarity of the day, the rest of us had overlooked the important point of how we would get home, as Diesel's dad was busy that night and said that we would have to sort something out for ourselves, which was fair enough.

"Alright, Diese," I said, "take Smithy with you, and me, Chad, Larry and Murph will take care of ourselves. "

"Cheers lads," murmured Smithy, rubbing his muddy trainers on the grass.

"Come on then Smit," shouted Gazzer, walking hand in hand with Elsa.

With the five of them disappearing over the hill to the car park, and Sheeny on the verge of playing his last record, the four of us needed to give the matter of transport some thought. Larry and Chad had spent what money they had on burgers and chips, assuming that we would get a lift from one of the spectators, which was indeed lurking in the back of my mind, but the crowd was dispersing and the number of people to ask was decreasing.

As more questions than solutions occurred to me, one of Sheeny's 'runners' brushed past, giving me an idea. I flagged him down, explaining our problem, and asked if Sheeny would give us a mention over the microphone so as to get us a lift. He said that he would ask the DJ but could not make any guarantees.

After being informed of the situation, Sheeny glanced over towards us as he was putting his records away, and yelled with a smirk on his face, "Aren't you Smithy's mates. That really interesting lad who I was talking to today?"

The four of us smiled and waved, obviously embarrassed because our 'street cred' was being dinted somewhat. The host found our reaction most amusing, and with a roar of laughter, he bellowed down the microphone, "Can anyone take these four to Clough Lane in Salford. They're friends of Smithy, the Road Show Bore 1982!"

Many of the people still there cheered, and fortunately a lad tapped me on the shoulder, saying that he was passing the Lane and had space for us in his van. Relieved and most thankful, we squeezed into the back of the vehicle. It had no seats and the journey was bumpy, but it was taking us home and that is all we were bothered about. Larry joked that he had a horse to feed the next morning!

CHAPTER 18

'New arrival'

As spring arrives, so the house buyer awakens, and it was one such buyer who found his way into the Street with his family in early April '83.

The house at the bottom of Cromson Street near the school had been on the market for five or six months. Built only a few years previously, it was an impressive bungalow with a massive garden. It had 'well to do' written all over it and it was not surprising, therefore, when a family with what can only be described as 'deep pockets', moved in.

The last name of the family was Dean, and it comprised of Bartholomew Dean who worked in export and drove a brand new Porsche, his wife Henrietta who had a collection of hats that would put the Queen to shame and their son Tarquin.

We actually got to meet Tarquin on a rainy Saturday morning whilst kicking around a ball near the Wall. 'April fool's day' would have been a perfect opportunity to welcome him into the crew but unfortunately that had passed a week earlier! He walked over to us, carrying a brand new casey football. "Hello," he said, "my name is Tarquin. Do you have a football team? I'm not bad in midfield. "

He was very well spoken with a southern accent, typical of the home counties. I got the impression that he attended public school.

On hearing the question, Gazzer, Diesel and Smithy hid their grins by going into a 'team hug' around the football, and told old jokes so as to give themselves cover for their subsequent outbursts of laughter which had been obviously provoked by

Tarquin's presence. Larry and Chad smiled a little awkwardly, and yes, it was Murph who made the first contact with our new arrival.

"Football team? There is no football team. " he responded in the most succinct fashion possible.

It was true that the name Tarquin sounded a little odd, and his accent was different to what we were accustomed to in Salford. The question also was a little presumptuous, but the lad had done me no harm, so I tried to be at least civil to him. Hearing Murph's detailed reply to the question, I quickly interjected, "Are you new in the Street?" suspecting that he and his family were the new people who had just moved into the bungalow, but not knowing for sure at that point.

Tarquin seemed relieved that at least somebody was taking him seriously, replying, "Yes, my parents and I moved into the property at the bottom of the street five or six days ago. My father is the director of an export company and we needed to move from Kent to North West England because his company has relocated to Salford Quays. Now that we're fairly settled, my father thought it might be a good idea to meet some new friends. "

All I could hear while the lad was talking was suppressed laughter and sniggering, and the only way to get things on a more even keel was to throw his ball into the middle of the field and see if he could play football. Chad, Larry and I passed around the ball with Deany, which was his new nick name on the pitch, and eventually Gazzer, Diesel and Smithy joined in. Murph watched from the side lines.

Deany was good on the ball and sent over some good crosses which the others connected with, and sometimes converted into goals. He was also a natural with corners. The new ball was kicked around for a good hour and with every kick the 'huddle trio' gained more respect for Deany. However to say that they fully accepted him would not have been true. It would take time.

After the 'kick around', Deany said that he had to return home because he was going for dinner or lunch as he called it, at a country club with his parents. However, he asked if it would be alright to meet the following week after school for a chat at the Wall, to which we all nodded.

On the Monday and Tuesday, Deany bonded more with the boys, as they did with him. We showed him break dance, which apparently was not practised much on the streets of Kent. It was hilarious, watching him perform the caterpillar which looked more like a constipated snail, and whilst doing the salsa and Indian steps, he displayed moves which were different let us say.

However, on the Wednesday, I saw the interaction between the newcomer and some of the crew in a different light.

We decided to go to Harp Street to do a spot of fishing before it got dark. After seeing Deany's collection of five fishing rods which were all top of the range and fitted with high performance reels, Gazzer, Diesel and Smithy all asked if they could borrow a rod for the evening. They remarked that the experience of catching a tench with such a rod would be amazing. Diesel already had some decent gear, as we have seen, but Deany's tackle was better, much better.

Although the three of them had started to accept Deany as one of the lads, the request for the fishing rods made me wonder if they had another agenda.

Namely using him for his parents' wealth. Larry and Chad had shown no desire to take advantage of him, and neither had Murph, but the latter could easily change his ways when he eventually realised what was going on.

On the Thursday night, my suspicions were more or less confirmed when we all decided to play a few strokes of golf on the field. As you may recall, Diesel only had a driver which was falling apart and an old putter, and Gazzer used an ancient putter which had been dug out of the attic.

The two of them showed their aging clubs to Deany at the Wall before going to the field to play. They wiped imaginary tears from their eyes as they laughed, saying that their gear and the ark were made around the same time. If you read between the lines, this was an indirect request to borrow some of his clubs which were second to none. They even put Chad's equipment in the shade!

Deany clearly understood what the pair were hinting at because he responded in a most accommodating way. Rather than simply lending his own clubs to Gazzer and Diesel, he gave the two of them his father's golf bag for the evening, containing a full set of high quality irons and drivers! I have never seen the boys enjoy their golf so much. It was at this juncture, that Murph also became aware of the rich pickings, and helped himself to the equipment of Deany's dad without even asking our new addition, so it seemed.

All this activity led to an interesting invitation, given at the Wall on the following evening. Deany's mum and dad had an apartment in Nice in France, and they went there for the weekend once a month. It so happened that they were going that coming weekend, and Deany invited all of us to his house for a 'sleepover' on the Saturday night and dinner in the early afternoon. It did not take much persuasion for the seven of us to accept and on Saturday evening, we all gathered outside his gate at six o'clock, armed with sleeping bags and a bottle of whiskey!

After a brief exchange of words, I knocked on Deany's door, the brass head of the lion bouncing off the plate underneath. He opened the door with a smile on his face, waving the key to the house. "It's all ours tonight," he said with a grin, "we'll have a ball!"

We all laughed as we piled in, but I did wonder if the lads who had previously taken advantage of Deany would carry on doing so during the stay. He was a little 'wet behind the ears', having led a sheltered life, I suspected, and he still had not realised what they were up to. He obviously thought that 'share and share alike' was what friends did, and therefore gave the fishing rods and golf clubs without a second thought. However would this point of view still be in tact at the end of the 'sleepover'?

"I've got a video!" exclaimed the host, running to the shelf above the wide screen, the size of which we had never seen before.

"What's that then?" shouted Gazzer, throwing his sleeping bag on one of the sofas.

"The F1 race at Brand's Hatch a few days ago," he replied. "It's really exciting!"

Although a few of us liked Formula One, the majority of the boys showed no real enthusiasm to watch it, and looked at Diesel who, as they knew, had a more interesting alternative. He pulled a video out of his torn plastic carrier bag and held it up for all to see, receiving a huge cheer from everybody except

Deany who looked somewhat disheartened, as he put the F1 video back on the shelf.

"The Life of Brian!" yelled Smithy. "Love it. So funny!"

"I'm Brian and so is my wife!" quoted Chad from the film, arousing guffaws of laughter.

The whisky bottle was passed around as Diesel put on the video, and everybody took their seats. Deany brought a stool out the kitchen and placed it at the side of the coffee table because both of the sofas were full. He did watch the video but with no real interest, only laughing in the correct places so as not to appear as the odd one out.

Murph was indeed a little slow off the mark when it came to seeing the opportunities that Deany's lifestyle had to offer, but he more than made up for it that night.

"Has your dad got a drinks cabinet, Deany?" he asked, turning round to speak to the host.

"Yes," replied Deany, "its at the bar in the conservatory. "

When the lads heard the word 'bar', Diesel put the video on pause.

"He's got a bar?" yelled Gazzer with glee.

"Yes, but. . . " replied Deany, who did not have time to finish the sentence because everybody except Larry, Chad and myself, sprinted almost immediately to the back of the house in pursuit of spirits, beer and whatever else they could get their hands on.

It was at this moment that the lad's innocent outlook of life in the Street shattered and lay in pieces on the floor.

"They're just after what they can get, Tod, aren't they? They don't want my friendship. They're more interested in my father's drink cabinet. "

I did not reply, and neither did Larry or Chad, because although what he was saying was not completely correct, there was some truth in it.

"Listen, the three of you, at least you did not scurry off with the intention of plundering my father's cabinet like the rest, so have a drink with my blessing. There is also a full box of meat pies in the fridge which were bought for tonight, but I guess they'll find them without needing to speak to me. I'm going to bed. Let the others know if they wonder where I am, which I'm sure they won't. "

I simply nodded as the others did.

"He's a decent kid," said Larry. "They'll run riot tonight. "

"We can't do anything more, Laz," I replied. "Let's say that we're off Deany's Christmas card list. Why don't we just get pissed like he said. "

Gazzer soon returned back with a full bottle of whisky and Diesel was holding a bottle of vodka. Murph had found a crate of lager, and Smithy had a box of cheese and onion crisps in one hand and four cans of bitter in the other. The relationship with Deany was dead in the water so Larry, Chad and I took a can of lager from Murph and got merry with the others as we carried on watching the video.

"What have the Romans ever done for us?" shouted Smithy, quoting another line from the film, as he cracked open a can of bitter.

"The drains perhaps!" cried Gazzer, guzzling the bottle of whisky with a grin.

All four of them did ask where Deany was, and when I said that he had gone to bed, they just gave a look of surprise because it was early, and then continued to watch the film. It was only a few days later when we told them what Deany had said, that they realised how much upset they had caused!

It did not take Murph too long to find the meat pies and they were soon turning in the microwave, before being splattered with tomato sauce.

We played the film three times. It may seem a little excessive but it was hilarious as it still is today. Outbursts of laughter intermingled with the clinking of glasses, the cracking of ring pulls and, of course, the voices of Python filled the room until the early hours of the morning.

Why we brought sleeping bags, I do not know because the next morning, we were all sprawled over the sofas and the floor without them, the trailer for the video going in a loop.

As we saw the ransacked house in the light of day, we all came to the conclusion that it would be a good idea to leave the house as quickly as possible and that is exactly what we did. There would be no invite to Sunday dinner, that was certain.

Deany and his parents left the street a few weeks later. Their departure did not surprise me, but I did not think that they would have vacated the bungalow so soon. The estate agent who was showing the empty property to prospective buyers, said that they had moved to Cheshire as Salford boys, according to Mrs Dean, were the roughest and toughest in the Greater Manchester area and were not the right material for her son to mix with. It was a good job in that case, I thought, that the paths of Deany and Rammy never crossed!

CHAPTER 19

'CB radio'

The wild month of June '83 with the hedge hopping, the 'narking' and all the rest, decelerated a little, once we got into July due to Larry's investment in a Citizen Band Radio or 'CB' which were just coming into fashion at that time. All the final exams were finished by this point and Larry thought it might be an idea to have a pastime, when he was not taking care of Snow Flake of course, which did not involve the possibility of ending up in a borstal while he waited for his 'O' level results. His 'handle' or name on the air was the 'Milkman' and he chatted with 'breakers' all over the north west of England.

Just as they had done the year before, Larry's parents jetted off to Greece again in the second week of July, leaving their son at the helm with a power 'mic' in one hand and a tin of beans in the other!

Not surprisingly, it was not long before he invited us to the house for a few drinks and, of course, to spend some time on the 'rig' which was the name that 'breakers' gave to their radio set.

He said that there were decent 'breakers' on the airways with whom you could have good conversations, but there were also 'dipsticks' whose sole intention was to ridicule other 'breakers' and talk complete hogwash. One such individual was a lad called the 'Hiker'. Larry had not seen this character face to face or 'eyeballed' him as the term was, but the 'breakers' who had met him said that he was a spindly guy with mousy blond hair in a perm and a face full of freckles. His real name was Alan.

It was only a short time before we heard the 'spanner' on Larry's 'rig' one night. The 'Hiker' was talking to a 'breaker' called 'Secret Agent' who was trying to have a conversation about cars with him. However, once he had completed what he had to say, Alan would say 'breaker break' and refer to his 'chat buddy' as 'Secret Squirrel'. The latter tried to correct Alan on various occasions, but he continued to mock the 'handle', chortling as he did so.

"Bit of a tool, that 'Hiker' bloke isn't he?" commented Gazzer with a grin.

"You're not kidding," said Diesel, "but we could take the piss out of him a treat. It would be simple and a right laugh. "

"What have you got in mind?" asked Smithy gleefully.

"Chad," said Diesel, "any chance that Suzy can come down here with you tomorrow. I've got an idea on how to wind that dipstick up. "

"Don't see why not Diese, I think she's free. "

After listening to a little more drivel from Alan, we all called it a night and made tracks home, an interesting evening ahead of us, the next day.

Suzy did indeed make an appearance at Larry's house, the following evening, and fortunately the 'Hiker' was on the airwaves, 'winding up' another 'breaker'. All the ingredients were ready. Only a blender was needed. Diesel asked Suzy to join in with the conversation that the 'Hiker' was having, and to give the impression that she really fancied Alan after seeing pictures of him that other 'breakers' had taken on 'eyeballs'.

After a little coaching from Larry, she took the 'mic' and began the 'wind up'. "On the side," she said, a little unsure of herself, and then repeated the request with more confidence.

"Side, come on in," responded the 'Hiker'. "What's your handle, crazy lady?"

Suzy looked a little shocked that somebody she did not even know was calling her a crazy lady. However, she paused for a moment and carried on with the brief. "My handle," she replied, looking at the scribble on her cigarette box, "is Yellow Rose. "

"Why's that?" inquired the 'Hiker', "because you're beautiful like a rose, no doubt. " He giggled in his squeaky voice.

"Well, the thing is," replied Suzy, looking at Chad with a smile, "a breaker showed me a picture of you today that she took at an eyeball, and you look a bit of alright. " She gripped Chad's hand really tight to stop herself from laughing and then added, "I was wondering if you fancied an eyeball. " After clicking off the 'mic', Suzy fell about laughing, like the rest of us, and missed Alan's reply. She eventually composed herself as best as she could and asked Alan to repeat himself, claiming that she had momentarily lost the signal.

"I said," giggled Alan, "as long as you're fit, I'll meet you any time."

"Oh, you won't be disappointed," responded Suzy, holding back her laughter, "once you get an eyeful. "

As the 'Hiker' spoke some twaddle in reply to Suzy's comments, we all howled with laughter, just catching the last part of his response, saying where he wanted to meet her and at what time. Larry scrawled the details on a scrap of paper to make sure that she had not missed anything.

"OK, then," she continued, as calmly as she could, with a glance at the piece of paper, "I'll see you at the petrol station in town in a couple of days at around seven o'clock. "

"No problem," answered the 'Hiker' with a chuckle. "This is breaker break on a date. The Hiker, signing out. "

"What a tool!" shouted Gazzer, fighting to get his words out for laughing.

"Do you know anyone who'll do it, Suzy?" asked Chad, red in the face, after having busted a gut, as we all had.

"Jill will be up for it. She loves ripping the piss out of blokes, especially spanners like him. Leave it to me. "

I had seen Jill only on one occasion and quite frankly, that was enough. She was well over six foot, looked like the back of a bus and carried a bit of 'timber' let us say. She would scare Alan to death and I wanted to be there with Chad's binoculars when it happened. From the reactions of the others, they were of the same opinion!

The following night, we just 'earwigged' to see if the 'Hiker' would comment on the 'eyeball' arranged for the next day. We eventually found him on one of the channels talking claptrap as usual. He told other 'breakers' that he had 'got off' with a beauty called 'Yellow Rose' who he was meeting in town for a date. He built her up into a beautiful princess, and the more he did so, the further he strayed from reality.

"He's going to collapse with shock when he sees Jill tomorrow," remarked Smithy. We all laughed as we put our coats on to leave. It was going to be a good one, I was convinced of it.

The lads met at Larry's the next day at six o'clock or thereabouts for a quiet coffee before the event, and we were soon joined by Suzy and Jill. The girls laughed and joked, saying that Alan would be begging for a bus to stop, by the time Jill had finished with him! We walked to town full of anticipation, Chad holding tightly onto his binoculars. Murph mentioned the need of a good hiding place so as not to miss any of the action. I informed him that the thought had occurred to me and a location had already been planned. We were, in fact, going to hide behind the church wall which faced the petrol station. Jill was going to make sure that the 'Hiker' was directly under a light on the forecourt of the station, so we could see each and every expression.

As we settled behind the wall, Chad spotted a thin guy with a perm appearing on the forecourt. After a quick look through the 'bins', I signalled to Jill on the other side of the road that the 'target' had arrived. The binoculars were being passed constantly from one to the other.

When Jill approached Alan, the lad looked traumatised. You could have knocked him over with a feather. She started to put her hands all over him as she tried to engage in conversation. We roared with laughter so much that I am surprised that he did not hear us.

"Not so sure of himself now!" cried Gazzer.

"He's a tool!" spluttered Suzy.

He repeatedly looked at his watch, trying to give an excuse to leave. She endeavoured to talk to him for a further four or five minutes, never ceasing to paw him, and then kissed Alan on the cheek, splitting her sides as she walked off. You have never seen a bloke so relieved to see the back of a girl, and the 'Hiker' sprinted away while the going was good.

The encounter was priceless. It creased us up so much that we could not walk home in a straight line. Jill said that a 'wind up' had never gone so well.

The 'Hiker' did not visit the airways for a few days after his experience with Jill, which gave us a chance to talk to the lady 'breakers' without having him bothering us whilst we were chatting. Gazzer and Diesel did not waste any time arranging 'eyeballs', of course, with several of them, and eventually whittled the girls down to two for the purpose of 'fun and frolics'. Gazzer was to be found in Darcy's hay shed with a pretty girl called Hazel who called herself the 'Lioness' on the airways, and Diesel found himself another nice looking girl called Francesca, whose 'handle' was 'Ice Lady'. The 'Hiker' had made advances towards Hazel in the past, without any success, and when Gazzer heard about the story, it gave him an idea for another 'wind up' with Alan.

There was a 'CB' meeting every Wednesday night in town which took place in a function room of a pub and was attended by many of the 'breakers' in the area.

Two or three days before the next meeting, Gazzer asked Hazel to flirt with Alan on air, so as to make him think that she had reconsidered. The plan then was to go to the meeting, where Hazel would 'eyeball 'the 'Hiker', lead him a merry dance and eventually leave with Gazzer. The important thing was that Alan got no hint of what was going on, so that Gazzer's appearance would have the maximum impact. It would be hilarious, and some of us thought that it could be even more amusing than the episode with Jill.

Hazel did request to join the chat whilst the 'Hiker' was on air, quite a few times, and in between flirting with him, she spun him a yarn about how she simply did not have time to see him previously but now her circumstances had changed. He swallowed it hook, line and sinker. Their conversations sent us into hysterics and Diesel, amongst others, had to run into the garden and offload his outbursts there so that the 'Hiker' did not suspect anything.

We all turned out for the meeting on the Wednesday night, not surprisingly, Suzy included. Hazel and Francesca were going separately to the function room so as to maintain the 'smoke screen' with the 'Hiker'.

During our time on the 'rig', we had only known the 'breakers' by their voices, so we could only guess what they looked like. Now that we had both the voices and the faces at the meeting, their appearances sometimes did not match the images that we had originally conjured up, and it was a little weird to say the least.

After speaking to a few of the 'breakers', we found a table fairly near to Alan and the few mates who were with him, so that we could see everything. However we did not put ourselves too close to him that our cover was in jeopardy.

Hazel and Francesca soon appeared in the room and made their way to Alan and his cronies. The 'Lioness' teased Alan for a good hour, laughing and smiling with him, touching his curly hair and talking to him none stop. He looked relaxed and utterly content but this would prove to be short lived.

"When Gazzer gets up there," muttered Diesel, "that 'Hiker' bloke won't know what day it is. You thought he was shocked with Jill. He'll be on his back when all this is over. " We all broke down in laughter, looking towards the bar to avoid drawing his attention.

"This will teach the little shit that he doesn't own the airways," said Smithy bitterly.

We all grinned as Gazzer got up and walked towards Hazel. He took her by the hand and the pair engaged in French kissing right in front of Alan and his mates. Hazel even dropped her bag so that she was more comfortable in the act.

The 'Hiker' was overcome with trauma, looking somewhat flimsy in appearance. The two or three mates that he had there, were trying to bring him round as he was slumped in his chair.

The whole lot of us were falling around laughing, no longer caring if Alan saw us or not because obviously the 'wind up' had now been done.

After the display of passion, Diesel quickly got up and put his arm around Francesca, and the two lads left the function room with their lady 'breakers', winking to us as they went. The evening had been absolutely hilarious. Suzy said that she could not decide which was the funniest out of the two 'wind ups' because they both creased her up 'big time' as she put it. One was as good as the other as far I was concerned.

When Larry's parents returned from their holidays, we hardly ever went on the 'rig' again, because his mum and dad were not keen on a gang of lads running around in their home, which I can understand. However, Larry told us that the 'Hiker' did not use his 'CB' as much after the meeting in town, but when he did, he spoke to people with more respect and refrained from 'winding' them up, most of the time!

CHAPTER 20

'Diesel's birthday'

We had great fun with Larry's 'rig' in July '83 and consequently the month raced by, giving way to August before we knew it.

At the beginning of the month, it was Diesel's birthday, and his dad had kindly paid for all seven of us to have a meal at the curry house in town for his sixteenth, and also bought tickets for us to enter the bowling alley not far away from the restaurant. We had obviously eaten curries before, but none of us had ever been to this restaurant which had a reputation for making hot ones. It was the Saturday before the exam results were out, and the whole crew met at the Wall around ten o'clock in the morning. It was going to be a full day and if we survived it, an interesting evening.

Chad turned up with a bottle of whisky that his dad had bought for us. He had advised his son to be discreet as it would not go down too well with his mum if she found out about the transaction at the off licence! Larry threw a box of lager against the Wall, adding, "You can thank the old man for the lager. He got it for me because he thinks that I'm leaving the milk round when we get our results next Thursday, but he's got me for a whole lot longer yet before I qualify for the ambulances!" Darcy's heart was in the right place, of that there was no doubt, but he was just a grumpy old toad.

I managed to get a few cans out of the cellar and Smithy lifted a bottle of vodka from his dad's spirit cabinet. He said that the cabinet was full of bottles and the vodka would not be missed.

The scene was set and we drank from tumblers kindly supplied by Gazzer, who had smuggled them out of his mum's cupboard. Murph, incidentally, arrived with a box of salt and vinegar crisps under his arm. I do not know which trailer they fell off!

Talk about curry, not surprisingly, was top of the agenda.

"I think a Madras for me tonight," commented Gazzer as he finished his tumbler of lager, and reached for another can.

"Well, it's my party," laughed Diesel, "so I must lead from the front. A Vindaloo will be my request!"

We all laughed as Murph suddenly interjected, "Vindaloo? That's tame Diesel. You want to go for the Phall like me. Vindaloos are for novices!"

"You think so?" exclaimed Diesel, grinning. "After your first mouthful, you'll be on the floor mate with a waiter stood over you, holding a fire extinguisher!"

Amidst the laughter, a familiar dog appeared without warning at the corner of the Wall, followed by our friend 'Johnny-know-it-all'. He looked at us disapprovingly, and then at his watch. "A little early to be on the booze, isn't it lads?" he inquired. "No wonder we see strange behaviour from you. "

"It's my birthday, Mr Walton," answered Diesel. "We're going for a curry tonight. I'm having a Vindaloo. "

A smirk developed on Diesel's lips as he put the tumbler to his mouth. Gazzer smiled at his mate as he finished pouring the rest of the lager into his cup.

"When I was a teenager, I also liked to have a drink with the lads for a special event," noted Johnny. "I would get a little boisterous as you lot will, no doubt, today, but I did it behind closed doors where I did not disturb anybody. If I was that age now, I'd drink you all under the table and still not be a nuisance to the neighbours. "

I could see in the corner of my eye that Murph was acting a little suspiciously and possibly preparing for a moony which would have enhanced an already amusing encounter with Johnny, that was true, but at the same time, it would have wrecked the morning at the Wall. The chase would have displaced us from our perch for the rest of the day.

"You're an example to us all, Mr Walton," I commented quickly, more to distract Murph than anything else. His reaction was so funny. He shook his stick, whistled to the dog and growled, "Don't forget it my friend, don't forget it!"

"What a tool," whispered Smithy as our buddy walked on. We kept a lid on our laughter until Johnny boy had turned the corner, and then we let it all out, rolling in the aisles.

We stayed at the Wall until about two o'clock, talking about things that we had done during the year, whilst draining the spirit bottles and the cans of lager. We laughed about the chase with the fat policeman during the hedge hopping, the trauma on the 'Hiker's' face at the pub and the pursuit of Diesel by the police on his crosser, amongst other things. It was the story about the Moss that prompted Diesel to suggest a visit there to sober up a little for the curry that evening. Not wanting to spoil the Vindaloo, we all agreed that it was a good idea and made our way to the slag heaps.

The seven of us watched a few bikers racing up and down the hills on their crossers. "When I'm older," said Diesel, slurring his words a little, "I'll bring my son here and we'll go crossing together on our bikes. "

"You love it here, don't you Diese," said Gazzer, patting his mate on the back with a grin.

Diesel just smiled and carried on observing the activity on the slag. Whether it was the alcohol or the occasion, or perhaps both, he was showing the softer side to his character which he rarely did.

The time at the Moss did clear our heads slightly and by the time we had showered and put on a change of clothes, we were heading towards sobriety.

On the way to the curry house, the lads and I sang 'happy birthday' to Diesel which attracted some attention from a couple girls who were walking in the opposite direction over the road. One of them crossed over, and after asking who the birthday boy was, she kissed Diesel on the lips, saying that if she bumped into him again during the evening, there might be a bit more on offer. This obviously brought a huge grin to Diesel's face and he remarked that his Vindaloo would taste twice as good after such an encounter!

The music in the curry house was very relaxing and the waiter showed us to our seats. As was mentioned earlier, the restaurant did have a reputation for making hot curries, so it was reassuring to see the table laden with carafes of water, as the boys would obviously be challenging each other to see who could eat the spiciest dish.

As the waiter approached with his note pad and pencil, Murph started the contest. "I'll have a Phall please, and make sure that the chilli and peepers are red hot," he said with a smile that would soon disappear, I was sure, when he started to eat the food.

"A Vindaloo for me," said Diesel, sipping some water, "and an extra jug of this!" he added pointing to the glass.

"And I would like a Madras!" announced Gazzer, looking menacingly at Murph who was too busy in his own world to even notice.

So these were the three big contenders for the title 'Mr Curry 1983'. Chad and I had a Tikka Masala which is classed as a medium curry, so they tell me, and Smithy and Larry had a Dhansak which is of similar strength. If the 'big guns' fell at the first fence, which was a distinct possibility, hearing the stories about the restaurant, then one of us in the medium band could win. It would be interesting.

The Vindaloo and the Madras came out first. Gazzer started to struggle with his curry after four or five mouthfuls, needing to drink copious amounts of water and going extremely red in the face. Diesel was not comfortable either, going through a pile of serviettes as he blew his dripping nose. The Tikka Masala and the Dhansak were next served. Although the Masala was hot, Chad and I could just about cope, with a little help from the carafes of water, of course. Smithy, however, was well out of his depth, and after a couple of attempts at the Dhansak, he put the plate to one side, claiming that he had eaten a sandwich before coming out, and it had spoilt his appetite. The comment provoked much laughter around the table, and it was embarrassment that made him go red in the face, not the curry. Larry 'limped along' with his Dhansak, but he endeavoured to eat it as best he could.

The 'star' of the show, Murph, had still not received his curry and he drank his water with glee, whilst watching most of us wrestle with our food. "They always save the best til last," he joked, thumbing through the menu.

We all watched for the Phall to come through the swinging doors and finally it did. The waiter warned that it was a hot curry as he was serving it, but Murph did not really take much notice. However, he did take notice when he started to shovel the Phall into his mouth, and the reaction was absolutely hilarious. We split ourselves laughing. His face went a strange scarlet colour and he coughed and spluttered, nearly choking at one point. Pouring a full jug of water down his throat, he tried desperately to put out the fire that was burning him up. The waiter brought him a glass of milk and asked me if he was allergic to curry. I replied that the only thing that he was allergic to were brainwaves, and not to worry because he was just a 'dipstick'.

As he slowly recovered, so the roar of laughter subsided, and a few of us patted him on the back, advising that he should have a mild Korma next time. As we were leaving, we decided collectively that Chad met the challenge of eating a hot curry in the most convincing manner, and was declared the winner of the contest. From his reaction, however, I don't think that he was bothered either way!

Our throats were still burning and our 'street cred' had not yet fully recovered as we entered the bowling alley. However, it had been a laugh in the curry house, especially when Murph underestimated the Phall. The lads agreed, myself included, that we would do it again but perhaps change our options the next time!

As the pins fell amidst the joking and laughter, the battle with the curries soon faded away. Towards the end of the night, we were approached by a gang of lads who thought that they could handle a bowling ball better than us, so we had a competition to see if they were of the correct opinion. It turned out that their thoughts were misguided when we beat them most convincingly. Gazzer said that they were all 'spanners' and it was a waste of time playing them because they could not throw a ball for toffee, which we all agreed was fair comment.

Unfortunately Diesel never crossed paths again with the girl who gave him the kiss. However, he said that he really enjoyed his birthday because he did not stop laughing all day and even found a little time for reflection.

CHAPTER 21

'Christmas'

It is true that part of the day was taken by the milk round on the run up to Christmas '82 for Larry, Smithy and myself, but that did not stop us from having a good time with the others during the festive season, of course.

We did a spot of carol singing, 'snow bombing' along Clough Lane, made a snowman for Suzy and had an enjoyable Christmas Eve party.

Larry was a lad of many talents and this included his skills with a trumpet. He was a member of the town band and played first trumpet there on a Tuesday night. He often joked that he ought to make some money out the instrument at such times as Christmas, but he never did. This changed, however, in mid-December of that year when Gazzer, Diesel and Murph were talking of how 'broke' they were for Christmas.

"I don't know what I'm going to do for booze this Christmas," remarked Gazzer. "I haven't got a pot to piss in."

"Yes," agreed Diesel, "we need to get a few coins together, that's for sure."

"Without any bread, we can't get anything," added Murph, showing his powers of deduction as always.

"We could always do some carol singing," suggested Smithy, rolling a piece of snow up in his worn out gloves.

"Yes," I replied, "but carol singers are ten a penny. People just shut the door in their faces."

"Not if there's something original about it," said Chad. "Something out of the ordinary like a trumpet. " He looked at Larry who smiled.

"OK, then," he grinned. "Let's see what we can do with it tomorrow night. I'll get some words printed out and get the notes I need for my clip stand. "

The following morning, we all met at the Wall at sixish and Larry dished out the words of 'Once in Royal David's City' and 'We Wish You a Merry Christmas', suggesting that we alternate them so as not to bore the audience, and more importantly, ourselves. During the short rehearsal, it became apparent that Gazzer and Diesel simply could not sing, Murph sounded tone deaf and Smithy resembled an alley cat that had just met another one on it's patch. Chad and I would not get a glowing report either. What a shower, I thought. Hopefully the trumpet would drown the noise out.

We decided to perform on Clough Lane because there were lots of houses there, and the traffic would work alongside the trumpet to cover up the racket. A fresh blanket of snow covered the pavement that night because it had been snowing all day, and it crunched under our boots as we walked from house to house.

One bloke opened the door and started laughing openly when he heard us, but complimented the trumpet player, handing him a fifty pence piece. One woman got her husband because she thought that we could not possibly be a choir and the carol singing was a ploy to ultimately mug her. Needless to say, we got nothing there. Another man in his seventies opened the door, put his hand up to stop the Christmas carol and then asked the trumpet player to do a solo of 'Once in Royal'. He then told us of how he played the cornet in the army all over the world, and added that he would have been privileged to have played with Larry, as he put some money in the jar.

This was the general trend all evening as we went down the Lane. Coins were thrown into the jar that I was carrying, at a rate of knots, because of Larry's fabulous display on the trumpet and our pathetic contribution, which proved to be highly amusing. It was interesting that Gazzer and Diesel were keeping a note of the houses where we got nothing but a request to clear off, on a scrap of paper, stuffed into one of their pockets. It would soon be apparent why.

It was a fun filled night because we found our singing as comical as the majority of people at the door did. It was also very pleasant listening to the sound of the trumpet. The amount that we counted back at the Wall was thirty-two pounds which was divided between us. Gazzer breathed a sigh of relief when I passed him his share. "You're a life saver, Tod," he said, putting his thumbs up to Larry who nodded his head as he put the trumpet back into it's case.

The next evening, Diesel met us all at the Wall with a bottle of whisky in one hand and a piece of paper in the other. Gazzer recognised the scrap of paper straight away. "Aren't they the addresses of the miseries who told us where to go, yesterday evening, Diese?" he inquired.

"That's right Gaz," replied Diesel, "and tonight they're going to get their comeuppance. "

"What do you have in mind, Diese?" I asked.

"The snow has now turned into ice on the pavement so we can't use that. But the roadway has been treated. How about if we run down Clough

Lane on the road and 'snow bomb' all the tight arses who would not drop a coin in the jar last night. Are we all in?" he asked.

We all nodded our heads. Although Chad's response was the same , he did not look as committed as the others, but he stayed with us and listened to Diesel's plan. "We can each make four snowballs at the top of the Lane," he continued, "and put them in our pockets. You'll then run down the Lane behind me on the road and I'll point to the houses that need doing, shouting it's number. The first person will throw a snowball at the first house and then the second person in line will throw their snowball at the second house and so on. In this way, we rotate and do as many houses as we can in one go. There are about twenty of them. "

Spoken like a true General, I thought. Napoleon would have been proud!

Smithy looked over Diesel's shoulder, putting his computer game into his coat pocket, as he examined the house numbers. "There's one we have to be careful with, Diese," he said, "number seventy-eight where Jimmy McClean lives. He can run. "

"I did think of that," grinned Diesel, "but everybody who put two fingers up to us, needs to be served. We can't be seen to be prejudiced, can we? He's one of the last ones anyway. "

"Ready?" shouted Diesel over the laughter. We all gave the thumbs up and he charged down the Lane, pointing to houses and shouting numbers, with the six of us running behind him. After each instruction followed a little 'thudding' sound as the snow hit the door. Revenge was sweet and we howled with laughter as we carried out the task.

However, the laughing stopped for a while, when Jimmy's door was hit, because unlike most of them, he responded to our 'call' and sprinted down the roadway at some speed in pursuit of us. Black ice had formed on the surface of the road, though, where the railway bridge was on the Lane. We slowed down because we were aware of this, but Jimmy did not know about the problem and pelted over the bridge. He lost his grip, slipped and went flying onto the icy pavement, face first.

We obviously did not wait around to find out what happened, but we later heard that he sprained his ankle. I, personally, felt a bit sorry for bloke, but at least there were no broken limbs.

Four or five days after the 'snow bombing', we got heavy snowfall which led to an interesting request from Suzy at the Wall. "I've got a deal for you," she said, hand in hand with Chad, as we were talking about our plans for Christmas Day. "You make me a massive snowman in my front garden, and I'll throw a party at my house on Christmas Eve. My mum and dad are spending the eve at my nan's so the house will be free. "

"Can we get Yvonne and Wendy down?" asked Gazzer.

"They're my friends," responded Suzy, "and they're always welcome. "

She looked at me, for a moment, knowing that I was thinking about Petra, but I said nothing. Wiping her eyes slightly, she asked, "Well, are we going ahead?"

There was no problem with buying the booze for the party because we had just been paid for the carol singing and Smithy, Larry and I were working for Darcy anyway. We nodded enthusiastically and the next day, we went to her front garden armed with shovels, an old hat and scarf that Murph had found in his grandad's shed and a carrot that Larry had got out of Snow Flake's stable.

Gazzer and I rolled a ball of snow in the street to make the head and Diesel and Smithy did the same to make the body. Once he was fitted together, Frosty, as Suzy called him was huge. Murph dressed Frosty with his hat and scarf and Larry and Chad did the finishing touches with the eyes and the nose.

It took us all day to make Frosty, but Suzy loved him and at the Christmas Eve party, the following night, Chad took countless pictures of people stood or sat with her new friend.

The party itself was a scream, with plenty of food, drink and merriment. Yvonne and Wendy did go to the party but Suzy made it clear that the bedrooms were out of bounds! I believe that the four of them went to Darcy's hay shed later in the evening. At least it had a roof, if nothing else, to keep the snow out.

CHAPTER 22

'Years later'

Those were our days at the Black Wall and I think that it is fair to say that those were, personally, the most care less times of my life, when life was such a hoot and I had nothing to worry about.

I am not saying that I preferred that stage of my life to what it is at the moment because I am very happy, as we speak, with my girlfriend of twenty-one years and my twelve year old son. However, it was a different type of existence that I will always look fondly upon. There were the chases where we almost collapsed in laughter, the break dancing that aroused such contentment, and the rides of exhilaration on the crosser, but to name a few. The times that I had with the lads on the Street were what kept me going as a teenager. It kept me happy, it kept me vibrant, it kept me alive.

I am not suggesting either that I did not like school. It was OK, and indeed the 'O' levels that I got there paved the way to my post as a chemist for a large pharmaceutical company. However, I did not look forward to school as much as I looked forward to being at the Wall, where thrills and excitement were in abundance.

I have only passed it two or three times since the eighties, and each time a tear appears in my eye as my years there flash before me. So what happened to the others?

Smithy passed five 'O' levels at school, and after going to college to do an IT course, he got a job in computer software, not surprisingly. He is married with three children. He did bore us a little from time to time on the Street with his lectures and jargon. He also demonstrated behaviour which was somewhat delusional now and then, but he was a laugh. Whether this was always with him as oppose to at him is another story, but his heart was in the right place, and we must never forget that he saved Larry's life at the Raz.

Murph tried, on several occasions, to get a girlfriend, back in the day but never actually achieved his goal, not as far as I can remember, anyway. He almost succeeded at the road show but unfortunately the girl finally walked away. How things change! He is now married to a beautiful lady in Berkshire and is a team leader, working on fork lift trucks. The word is, that he is making a tidy sum for himself. Obviously, the time he missed at school did him no harm.

Diesel loved his crosser and the hay stacks amongst other things, and of course his dream was to be in the marines. He rides around Manchester on an impressive motorbike presently and has a different woman every weekend. No change there then. He sadly did not get into the marines but joined the regular army and reached the rank of sergeant, before leaving in 2015. As a Crommy Boy, he had no respect for authority or system. He hid that well from the army clearly! He was in the forces for over thirty years! He never had children.

Gazzer did get into the marines and is still there. He was involved in active combat for fifteen years and later became involved in recruitment in the south of England. He was dedicated to his aim of being a soldier. If he wanted to do something, he would do it and would do it well. However, he was no angel as has been clearly illustrated in the book! Gazzer is married with two sons, one of whom is currently in the marines also.

Chad did get the 'O' levels that he needed to go to technical college and became a mechanic, presently owning two garages in the midlands. He eventually got married to Suzy and they had a daughter together, who has since flown the nest. They live in Wolverhampton. He liked his high jinks on the Street when, of course, Suzy allowed it!

Larry was always the quieter one at the Wall, although he had his moments during some of the things we did. He did become an ambulance driver after leaving school with his five 'O' levels, and has worked in the profession ever since, dedicated to his role. In 2001, he married a male nurse from the hospital where he works in London and they live happily on the outskirts of the capital.

We all meet up in different pubs in Salford every five of six years. We laugh and joke and, I am sure, shed the occasional tear, as we fondly look back at the times we had at the Black Wall.